Key Stage 3

ENGLISH

Homework
Book

Authors – Jane Lodge and Paul Evans
Series Editor – Alwyn Morgan

Letts

EDUCATIONAL

Acknowledgements

This publication is dedicated to all parents who try to help their children with their homework, and all of those who might not necessarily seek to help, but still care dearly about their children's education.

I would also like to express my sincere thanks to the authors for responding so well to the challenge of producing these materials, and Letts Educational for their vision and commitment in promoting the role of parents in their children's education.

Finally, I would like to thank my wife, Carole, for her support, encouragement and patience.

Alwyn Morgan

Every effort has been made to trace copyright holders and to obtain their permission for the use of copyright material. The authors and publishers will gladly receive information enabling then to rectify any error or omission in subsequent editions.

First published 1998

Letts Educational, Schools and Colleges Division, 9-15 Aldine Street, London W12 8AW
Tel: 0181 740 2270, Fax: 0181 740 2280

© Text – Jane Lodge and Paul Evans 1998

Series Editor – Alwyn Morgan

Design and illustrations © BPP (Letts Educational) Ltd 1998

Design – Tessa Barwick and Dave Glover

Project Management – Rosine Faucompré

British Library Cataloguing-in-Publication Data

A CIP record for this book is available from the British Library

ISBN 1 84085 0175

Printed in Great Britain by Bath Press Ltd

Letts Educational is the trading name of BPP (Letts Educational) Ltd

CONTENTS

An Introduction for Parents and Pupils

1 The English National Curriculum   *v*
2 The National Test at the end of Key Stage 3   *vi*
3 Toolbox   *vi*
4 Summary of content of homeworks   *vii*
    List of words used in the teaching of English   119
    Glossary   121
    List of spellings   124

Activity	Page Number	Activity	Page Number
Rewarding Reading 1	2	Punchy Poetry 3	22
Rewarding Reading 2	3	Punchy Poetry 4	23
Rewarding Reading 3	4	Making a Drama Out of a Crisis 1	24
Rewarding Reading 4	5	Making a Drama Out of a Crisis 2	25
Rewarding Reading 5	6	Making a Drama Out of a Crisis 3	26
Rewarding Reading 6	7	Making a Drama Out of a Crisis 4	27
Explanations and Instructions 1	8	The Glamour of Grammar 1	28
Explanations and Instructions 2	9	The Glamour of Grammar 2	29
Explanations and Instructions 3	10	The Glamour of Grammar 3	30
Explanations and Instructions 4	11	The Glamour of Grammar 4	31
Words Around Us 1	12	Hard Sell, Soft Soap 1	32
Words Around Us 2	13	Hard Sell, Soft Soap 2	33
Words Around Us 3	14	Hard Sell, Soft Soap 3	34
Words Around Us 4	15	Hard Sell, Soft Soap 4	35
Radio Times 1	16	Voices From the Past 1	36
Radio Times 2	17	Voices From the Past 2	37
Radio Times 3	18	Voices From the Past 3	38
Radio Times 4	19	Voices From the Past 4	39
Punchy Poetry 1	20	Voices From the Past 5	40
Punchy Poetry 2	21	Voices From the Past 6	42

Activity	Page Number	Activity	Page Number
Comics and Magazines 1	44	Travel the World 4	79
Comics and Magazines 2	45	In the News 1	80
Comics and Magazines 3	46	In the News 2	81
Comics and Magazines 4	47	In the News 3	82
Soap Springs Eternal 1	48	Hair Today, Scone Tomorrow 1	83
Soap Springs Eternal 2	49	Hair Today, Scone Tomorrow 2	84
Soap Springs Eternal 3	50	Poetry, Please 1	85
Soap Springs Eternal 4	51	Poetry, Please 2	86
Hello, Shakespeare 1	52	Poetry, Please 3	88
Hello, Shakespeare 2	53	Poetry, Please 4	90
Hello, Shakespeare 3	54	Poetry, Please 5	92
Hello, Shakespeare 4	55	Poetry, Please 6	94
Different Writers, Different Voices 1	56	All The Better to Eat You With 1	95
Different Writers, Different Voices 2	58	All The Better to Eat You With 2	96
Different Writers, Different Voices 3	60	All The Better to Eat You With 3	97
Different Writers, Different Voices 4	62	All The Better to Eat You With 4	98
Different Writers, Different Voices 5	64	All The Better to Eat You With 5	99
Me, Myself, I 1	66	Spelling, Punctuation & Grammar 1	100
Me, Myself, I 2	67	Spelling, Punctuation & Grammar 2	101
Me, Myself, I 3	68	Spelling, Punctuation & Grammar 3	102
Grab That Grammar 1	69	Spelling, Punctuation & Grammar 4	103
Grab That Grammar 2	70	An Investigation into Human Nature 1	104
Grab That Grammar 3	71	An Investigation into Human Nature 2	106
Grab That Grammar 4	72	An Investigation into Human Nature 3	108
Argument Writing 1	73	An Investigation into Human Nature 4	110
Argument Writing 1	74	An Investigation into Human Nature 5	112
Argument Writing 3	75	Forms of Writing 1	114
Travel the World 1	76	Forms of Writing 2	115
Travel the World 2	77	Forms of Writing 3	116
Travel the World 3	78	Writing an Essay	118

AN INTRODUCTION FOR PARENTS AND PUPILS

1 ~ The English National Curriculum

The English National Curriculum has three Attainment Targets.

Attainment Target 1 is Speaking and Listening.

Attainment Target 2 is Reading.

Attainment Target 3 is Writing.

The National Curriculum describes what pupils in Years 7, 8 and 9 (or Key Stage 3) should learn in their English lessons.

In Speaking and Listening, pupils should:

- talk for all kinds of different purposes, such as to explain, to persuade and to analyse;
- talk in a range of different situations, both formal and informal;
- listen attentively and respond to what they have heard;
- take part in all kinds of drama and role-play;
- take part in discussions;
- use standard English fluently and accurately;
- consider how the use of words develops and changes in the English language.

In Reading, pupils should:

- read plays, novels, short stories and poems;
- read texts from other cultures and traditions;
- read some works by named authors who were writing before 1900;
- read non-fiction texts, like autobiographies, diaries and travel writing;
- investigate the media, such as newspapers, radio, television and film;
- analyse and evaluate what they read.

In Writing, pupils should:

- plan and draft their work;
- write stories, poems, scripts and non-fiction;
- take notes;
- learn spelling patterns and words which do not conform to a pattern;
- use neat, legible handwriting;
- understand and use grammar;
- use the full range of punctuation;
- use dictionaries and thesauruses.

2 ~ National Test at the end of Key Stage 3

In May of Year 9, most pupils in England and Wales sit national tests (often called SATs) in English, Maths and Science.

As a result of these tests, pupils and parents are given an indication of how well pupils are doing in those subjects. This indication is given in the form of a Level. Level 1 is the lowest; Level 8 is the highest. Pupils who are performing better than Level 8 can be given an Exceptional Performance grading.

By the end of Key Stage 3, most pupils will be performing within the range of Levels 3 to 7.

Also at the end of Key Stage 3, teachers report to parents the Level which they think a pupil has reached in day to day classwork. This may be the same as the Level which the pupil gained in the exam, or it may be different, for example if the pupil suffers from exam nerves, and so did not perform as well as expected on the day of the exam.

3 ~ Toolbox

To complete these homeworks, you will need:

Pen

Pencil

Ruler

Colour pencils

Eraser

A dictionary and a thesaurus will also be very useful.

4 ~ Summary of content of homeworks

Here is a summary of what is contained in all the homeworks in this book.

Homeworks 1-6 Rewarding Reading
Reading fiction at school and at home

Homeworks 7-10 Explanations and Instructions
Reading and writing instructions

Homeworks 11-14 Words Around Us
A look at the writing you come across in the world around you

Homeworks 15-18 Radio Times
Investigations into different types of radio programmes

Homeworks 19-22 Punchy Poetry
Practising some poetry writing techniques

Homeworks 23-26 Making a Drama out of a Crisis
Practising some drama techniques

Homeworks 27-30 The Glamour of Grammar
A look at audience, purpose, verbs, adjectives and sentences

Homeworks 31-34 Hard Sell, Soft Soap
A look at advertising

Homeworks 35-40 Voices from the Past
A look at non-fiction written before 1900

Homeworks 41-44 Comics and Magazines
A look at comics and magazines

Homeworks 45-48 Soap Springs Eternal
A look at soap operas

Homeworks 49-52 Hello, Shakespeare
An introduction to Shakespeare

Homeworks 53-57 Different Writers, Different Voices

A look at the variety of writing in English

Homeworks 58-60 Me, Myself, I

A look at diary writing and autobiography

Homeworks 61-64 Grab that Grammar

A look at adverbs, menu poems, punctuation and active and passive voices

Homeworks 65-67 Argument Writing

A look at argument writing

Homeworks 68-71 Travel the World

A look at travel brochures

Homeworks 72-74 In the News

A look at the language of newspapers

Homeworks 75-76 Hair Today, Scone Tomorrow

A look at the language of hairdressers and recipes

Homeworks 77-82 Poetry, Please

A look at some poetry written before 1900

Homeworks 83-87 All The Better to Eat You With

A look at different kinds of language, through the story of Little Red Riding Hood

Homeworks 88-91 Spelling, Punctuation & Grammar

A look at spelling, punctuation and the structure of sentences

Homeworks 92-96 An Investigation into Human Nature

A look at fiction written before 1900

Homeworks 97-100 Forms of Writing

A look at descriptive writing, letter writing and essay writing

Key Stage 3

ENGLISH

Homework
Activities

REWARDING READING 1

Aim:

~When you write up your findings, you will draft and summarise your own responses and those of others at home.~

National Curriculum:

~Speaking and Listening: Key Skills (a) confident self-expression~
~Writing: Key skills (b) non-fiction~

Background:

~This homework asks you to think about your history as a reader, and to see reading not only as something you have to do at school, but as part of everyday life~

Vocabulary:
different favourite question

Spellings:
accident accidental accidentally

Homework Activity 1

1 Think about the answers to these questions. Write down your answers in a way which is useful to you – perhaps as notes or in a chart.

- What can you remember about books before you learned to read?
- What can you remember about being read to when you were young?
- How did you learn to read?
- Who taught you to read?
- Can you remember any of the first books you read?
- What did you like reading at your last school?
- What are your favourite books?
- Why do you like them?
- Do you share books with anyone else?

2 Write your findings in the form of an interview or a newspaper article. Think of questions of your own which you could ask.

~ Ask the family ~

Ask others at home to answer the questions above. You might like to ask people of different generations, such as parents and grandparents. Do their answers differ from yours? Do they differ from each other?

Ask your own questions about reading.

REWARDING READING 2

Homework Activity 2

1 Consider the following questions, and write answers to them.

- What did you enjoy about the reading in this week's lessons?

- Why did you enjoy it?

- Why did you not enjoy it?

- What did you think of the plot of the book?

- What did you think of the characters?

2 Think about how you spend your leisure time.

- How much of it do you spend reading?

- What else do you do in your leisure time?

- Present your information in an appropriate form.

~ **Ask the family** ~

Ask people of different generations, such as parents and grandparents, to answer the questions above. Do their answers differ? Think of questions of your own which you could ask. Follow up the answers in your next question.

Aim:

~This homework encourages you to think about your reading and to write down your thoughts.~

National Curriculum:

~Speaking and Listening: Key Skills (a) organisation of what you say~
~Reading: Range (a) independent readers~
~Writing: Range (b) writing to develop thinking~

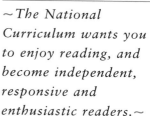

Background:

~The National Curriculum wants you to enjoy reading, and become independent, responsive and enthusiastic readers.~

Vocabulary:
encourage enjoy
explain

Spellings:
awful awfully

REWARDING READING 3

Aim:

~In this homework you will think about how characters behave and the reasons why they behave as they do.~

National Curriculum:

~Speaking and Listening: Range (a) exploration, argument, persuasion~

~Reading: Key Skills (b) motivation and behaviour of characters~

Background:

~One of the most important ways to talk about fiction is to think about characters, what they are like and why they behave as they do. You may have different opinions to your friends or family. Be prepared to argue for your point of view.~

Vocabulary:
behaviour
character   conclusion

Spellings:
already   although

Homework Activity 3

1 Think about a character from a book that you have been reading. Write about the character, considering the following questions.

- What does s/he do?

- What kind of person is s/he? How do you know?

- What do other characters think of her/him?

- What do you think of her/him?

- What would you think of her/him if you met her/him in real life?

- What do you think s/he will do in the part of the book you have not read?

- What do you think s/he will do with the rest of her/his life?

2 Create your own character. Write one paragraph to describe who the character is and what s/he does. Make him or her as unusual as you like.

- What do you think your character might do in a full length story?

~ Ask the family ~

Talk to someone at home about a character from a book. Encourage your helper to ask you questions. Find out what s/he thinks about the character. Does your helper have a favourite character from a book? What was so appealing about this character?

4

REWARDING READING 4

Homework Activity 4

1 Think about the plot of a story that you have read.

Now write about the plot. Imagine that you are writing for someone who has not read the story.

2 Think and write about the theme(s) of a story.

- What is the story about?

  Is it about:

| friendship? | fear? | hatred? |

- How has the author written about these themes?

- Think and write about the issues in the story. What problems do the characters face? How do they deal with them?

~ Ask the family ~

Tell someone at home the plot of the story. Make your account clear and interesting. Check that your helper has understood it.

Aim:

~This week you will think about how the plot develops, its twists and turns, its surprises. You will also consider the effect the story as a whole has had on you.~

National Curriculum:

~Speaking and Listening: Range (a) explanation, description, narration~

~Reading: Key Skills (b) development of plot and overall impact of text~

~Writing: Range (b) inform others through explanation, narration, paraphrase~

Background:

~We read a story to find out what happens. This is called the **plot** of a story.~

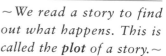

Vocabulary:
develop   effect
surprise   issues

Spellings:
address   addressed

5

Aim:

~This week you will think about the author of the book you are reading. You will consider the effect that s/he wanted to have on you when s/he wrote the story. ~

National Curriculum:

~Reading: Key Skills (b) distinguish between attitudes of characters and author~

Background:

~Sometimes authors like or admire a character, but sometimes they do not. You will need to think about how you can tell what an author really thinks. ~

Vocabulary:
behaviour character
conclusion

Spellings:
anybody anyone

Homework Activity 5

1 Think and write about the following questions.

In a story you have read, which characters does the author like and which does the author dislike? How do you know?

What does the author want you, the reader, to think and feel? How do you know?

2 Write a paragraph which describes a character. Show, by the way you describe him or her, that you dislike the character. Write a new paragraph about the same character which shows that you like him or her.

~ Ask the family ~

Discuss your answers to the questions above with someone at home.

Do they have any favourite authors?
What is appealing about these authors?

6

Homework Activity 6

1 Plan and write a few paragraphs of your own story.

- When you plan, make notes about your characters.

  Do not have too many characters! Three or four will be plenty.

- Decide on their names, ages and what kind of people they are. Try to create a contrast, for instance, make one character brave and another cowardly.

- Work out what will happen to them. Make it exciting, but do not make too many events happen: one main event will do. Decide how the story will end.

2 Write the rest of your story.

Keep to your plan! Do not ramble on! Make sure that the story has a satisfactory and convincing conclusion.

~ Ask the family ~

Talk about your plan with someone at home. Ask for comments on how it could be improved.

Read your story to your helper. Invite comments. Ask how it could be improved.

Aim:

~This week you will become an author yourself! You will put into practice everything you have learned over the last few weeks.~

National Curriculum:

~Reading: Standard English and Language Study (a) consider effects of organisation, structure, author's intentions~

~ Writing: Key Skills (b) develop ability to write narrative~

Background:

~ You will think about character, plot and your own intentions as an author!~

Vocabulary:
climax contrast
satisfactory exciting

Spellings:
advice advise

EXPLANATIONS AND INSTRUCTIONS 1

Aim:

~This homework asks you to read some instructions and then to put them in the correct order so that they make sense.~

National Curriculum:

~Reading: Range (e) wide range of non-fiction texts~

~Writing: Key Skills (b) distinctive ways of organising information~

Background:

~It is important to read and write all types of non-fiction. This homework asks you to practise your skills in sequencing information so that the final order of the material makes sense.~

Vocabulary:
instruction sequence

Spellings:
argue argument

Homework Activity 7

1 The following instructions are on how to paint a moorland scene but they have been mixed up. Read them carefully and put them in the right order.

a) While the wash is still wet, take a piece of tissue and blot unevenly over the blue area to make clouds.

b) Add more paint to the green wash to make it darker. Leave the distant mountain pale and paint the darker wash over the rest of the moorland area.

c) Finally, with the brush almost dry, add details of the railings and grass.

d) Clean your brush. Mix a pale wash of sap green and lay a flat wash of green over the moorland area.

e) Mix a pale blue wash and paint the sky.

f) First draw the outlines of the painting.

2 Think about one of your hobbies or interests. Make up your own simple set of instructions for one of them. Mix them up and ask someone else to put them in the right order.

~ Ask the family ~

Check with someone at home that you have put the instructions in a sensible order. If you have done Task Two, ask your helper to put your mixed-up list of instructions in the right order.

8

Homework Activity 8

1 Read these instructions and follow them.

a) Draw a line that measures 8 cm in length.

b) Draw another line exactly 6 cm above the first line.

c) Join up the lines at both ends to form a rectangle.

d) Draw a flower with 4 petals inside the rectangle.

e) Colour the flower red.

f) Draw a wiggly line under the rectangle.

g) Now draw a circle that is smaller than the rectangle.

h) Colour the circle yellow.

Write down how easy/difficult it was to follow the instructions. Could they be improved?

2 Make up a set of simple instructions that includes accurate detail.

Aim:

~*This homework helps you follow instructions accurately. This is an important life skill as well as a requirement of the National Curriculum. You will also be asked to assess how well the instructions were presented.*~

National Curriculum:

~*Standard English and Language Study (a) consider effects of organisation and structure*~

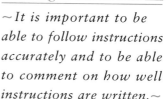

Background:

~*It is important to be able to follow instructions accurately and to be able to comment on how well instructions are written.*~

~ Ask the family ~

Ask someone at home to go through the drawing with you. If you have done Task Two, ask your helper to follow your instructions and to tell you what s/he thought of them. Ask your helper to give you a set of instructions. See if you can improve on them.

Vocabulary:
accurate comment

Spellings:
autobiography
biography

Aim:

~ This homework asks you to organise your own set of instructions into a list that would be easy for someone to follow.~

National Curriculum:

~ Writing: Range (b) to instruct~

Background:

~ In giving instructions it is important to be clear and detailed so that the person to whom you are giving the instructions can carry them out successfully.~

Vocabulary:
route
particular

Spellings:
bored
boring

Homework Activity 9

1 Think about exactly what you have to do to get to school. Perhaps you walk or take a particular bus, or perhaps you get a lift with someone.

Write down, in the right order, the things that you must do to get to school on time.

- If you walk, you should give detailed instructions on how to follow a route.

- If you get a bus, give details of time and bus routes and any walking necessary.

- If you get a lift, describe exactly what you do to get ready. Describe in detail the route that the driver must take.

Make sure that you do not leave out any important details.

2 Draw a map of the route that you follow to get to school. Include the road names and the names of buildings. The map should help someone to follow the route quite easily.

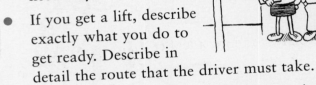

~ Ask the family ~

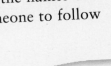

Look at the instructions you have written with someone at home. Ask your helper if you have left out anything. Change your work, if necessary, to correct any errors. Try writing instructions for someone at home to follow. Perhaps they could try to find something that you have hidden somewhere in the house.

Homework Activity 10

1 Choose an activity that you are familiar with.

Perhaps you like fishing, or painting, or in-line skating.

- Think about how you could write an explanation of how to do the activity.

  Be clear about where to start your explanation. Make sure you don't leave out any important detail.

- Write down your explanation. It might be helpful to do this in steps and to add pictures or diagrams to your explanations.

2 Turn your explanation into a leaflet that could be handed out to someone asking to know how to do the activity. This might take some time. If you have access to a computer you could use it do your leaflet. Remember, layout and presentation are important.

~ Ask the family ~

Check your explanation with someone at home. Are your diagrams and words clear? Is your helper able to carry out the activity? Can s/he suggest any improvements?

Aim:

~This homework builds on the work of the last three activities. You will write a clear explanation of how to do something that you already know how to do, for someone who does not know how to do it.~

National Curriculum:

~Writing: Range (b) explanation~

~Writing: Standard English and Language Study (b) organise whole texts effectively~

Background:

~This work puts together all the skills that you have been practising in the last three homeworks.~

Vocabulary:
explanation
presentation

Spellings:
beauty   beautiful

11

Aim:

~You will need to take careful note of your surroundings on your way to and from school.~

National Curriculum:

~Speaking and Listening: Range (a) describe and explain~
~Reading: Key Skills (c) evaluate how information is presented~
~Writing: Range (b) make notes~

Background:

~We are bombarded with information all the time when we are out on the streets. How aware are you of what is being presented to you?~

Vocabulary:
advertisement
bombarded   category
Spellings:
begin   beginning

Homework Activity 11

1 Look carefully at all the different kinds of written information that you see on the way to school. Make a note of each piece of writing you see. Be ready to present your notes and to talk about them in class.

2 Try to put the pieces of writing into categories, such as:

advertisements aimed at children

advertisements aimed at women

LOOK YOUNGER fast

advertisements aimed at men

SCHOOL

names

warnings

Organise your notes into the categories you create. Be ready to present your findings in writing and to talk about them at school.

~ Ask the family ~

Ask someone at home what s/he can remember about the writing in the area around your house. Ask which ones are particularly memorable and why.

Homework Activity 12

1 Think of the most effective advertisement you have seen on your way to school. What makes it effective? Is it:

a) the "catchy" words?

b) the pictures?

c) the interesting subject matter?

d) the size and colour of the words?

e) a combination of these factors?

• Design your own advertisement which you feel will make passers-by do what you want them to do.

2 Write about your advertisement. Explain what kind of people you are aiming your advertisement at, and why you have designed it as you have. Write about the impact that you hope the words and images will have.

~ Ask the family ~

Show your advertisement to someone at home. Imagine that your helper is from the company which makes the product and you are from an advertising agency. Convince the company that your advertisement will help sell more of their product!

Do they feel you can improve on your advertisement? Have they any favourite advertisements? What does the company find appealing about these advertisements?

Aim:

~ You are going to put yourself in the role of a worker in an advertising agency. You will need to think about how best to persuade passers-by to do what you want them to do.~

National Curriculum:

~ Speaking and Listening: Key Skills (a) construct persuasive arguments~

~ Writing: Key Skills (b) organise and express ideas and information in persuasive writing~

Background:

~ Now that you have looked at the way in which professional advertisers try to influence passers-by in the street, it's your turn to have a go!~

Vocabulary:
advertisement agency
image

Spellings:
belief believe believing

~ *In this homework you will analyse the material which comes through your letterbox at home.*~

National Curriculum:

~ *Reading: Standard English and Language Study (a) recognise features of different types of text*~

~ *Writing: Key Skills (a) use presentational devices*~

Background:

~ *We all get a lot of things through the post. In this homework, you will find out what kind of information comes through your letterbox.*~

Vocabulary:

category mail
post postperson
correspondence
analyse devise

Spellings:
busy business

Homework Activity 13
~ Ask the family ~

Ask an adult at home for permission before you start this task. Do not open any mail which is not addressed to you!

1 With an adult, sort through the mail which arrives at your house over a period of time – one day, two days.

Create a number of different categories. The categories might include:

- advertising from banks or building societies
- bills
- information about local events
- advertising from local shops.

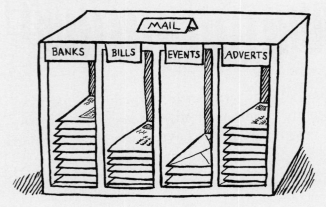

Sort the mail into "wanted" and "unwanted", and "requested" and "not requested" groups. List your categories, and record the items of mail in each.

2 Write a letter to the person who delivers your post, explaining which items you would like them to deliver in future and which items you would like them to throw away before delivery. Explain the reasons behind your choice. Do not post the letter!

Homework Activity 14

1 Find a piece of "junk mail" at home. It must be something which nobody at home wants, because you may want to cut it up and use certain parts.

- Find something positive about your piece of "junk mail". Stick it on to a clean piece of paper, and write next to it why you think that particular element is good.
- Now do the same again, finding something negative about a piece of "junk mail".

2 Create your own piece of "junk mail" which is so good that nobody will want to throw it away! Remember that the main point of "junk mail" is to persuade the reader to do something or buy something.

~ Ask the family ~

Involve someone at home in deciding what is good and bad about a particular piece of direct advertising. Try out your improved piece of advertising on your helper. What are his/her views on "junk mail"?

Aim:

~You will have to examine one piece of "junk mail" which has come through your letterbox, decide what is effective and what is not effective about it – and then improve on it.~

National Curriculum:

~Speaking and Listening: Key Skills (b) modify ideas in the light of what others say~

~Reading: Range (f) analyse and evaluate material~

~Writing: Range (c) write in range of forms~

Background:

~"Junk mail" is the name often given to direct advertising material that comes through the post.~

Vocabulary:
evaluate effective
"junk mail" referred

Spellings:
cause because

15

RADIO TIMES 1

Aim:

~In this homework you will listen to a radio commentary and write notes on what you hear.

You will need to listen carefully, notice what is said and how it is said, and then write down your observations as notes.~

National Curriculum:

~Speaking and Listening: Range (c) listen to a variety of media~

~Writing: Range (c) commentary~

Background:

~The National Curriculum stresses the importance of understanding how spoken language is used for different purposes.~

Homework Activity 15

1 Listen to a radio sports commentator commentating on a match/race/competition in progress.

Write down the answers to the following questions:

- What was the sport?
- What did you notice about how the speaker spoke (slow, fast, etc.)?
- Why did s/he speak this way?
- Could you hear any other sounds?
- If so, what effect did they have?
- Why are sport commentaries broadcast on the radio?

2 Listen to a commentator on the television describing a sporting event. Write notes on the differences and similarities between the radio commentator's style and the television commentator's style.

Vocabulary:
speech speaker
commentator

Spellings:
bring brought

~ Ask the family ~

Ask someone at home to listen to a sports commentary with you. Ask your helper what s/he thinks about the way spoken English is used. You may add your helper's ideas to your own.

Homework Activity 16

1 Read through the notes you made for Homework Activity 15. Now choose your favourite sport and think of one particular match/race/competition.

This could be a national or local event that you have seen or a made-up one involving you and your friends.

- Write one page of commentary on part of the event.

- Read your commentary aloud. Have fun! Make it sound as realistic as possible.

2 Make a tape recording of you reading your own commentary. Listen to the tape and write notes about how it sounds. Think about: pace (how fast you read); clarity (can you hear the words?); interest level (is it exciting to listen to?).

~ Ask the family ~

Read your commentary to someone at home, trying to sound like a real commentator. Ask your helper to tell you how well you did it and how you might improve it.

Aim:
~In this homework you will build on the work that you did last week to write your own commentary.~

National Curriculum:
~Speaking and Listening: Standard English and Language Study (a) speak with clear diction and appropriate intonation~

~Writing: Range (a) write for varied purposes~

Background:
~The National Curriculum stresses the importance of understanding how spoken language is used differently for different purposes.~

Vocabulary:
commentary dramatic soundwave

Spellings:
buy bought

RADIO TIMES 3

Aim:

~This homework asks you to think about ways in which spoken English and music are used to entertain and give information. You will also practise making notes.~

National Curriculum:

~Speaking and Listening: Key Skills (b) identifying tone and speaker's intention~
~Writing: Range (c) write notes~

Background:

~The National Curriculum stresses the need to be aware of how vocabulary and tone alter when the spoken word is used for different purposes.~

Vocabulary:
presenter   station
identification

Spellings:
careful   carefully

Homework Activity 17

1 Choose a radio station that plays music and has people speaking on it.

Listen to the way that the presenter speaks.

- What kind of words does s/he use?

- How does s/he speak? What sort of tone or mood is suggested by this?

- How much time is given to music compared with talk?

- Write notes in answer to these questions. What else is interesting in the way the programme is presented?

2 Listen to a different programme on another radio station. Write down what it is that you are listening to. Write notes on the differences and similarities between the programmes.

~ Ask the family ~

Find out which radio stations and programmes the people in your home like. Talk to them about why they listen to these stations. Present their answers as a display poster.

Homework Activity 18

1 Write a scene from a radio play about some kind of family argument. You might, for example, write about a teenager's untidy bedroom or an argument with a brother or sister. Try to make the scene realistic but interesting.

- Decide who your main characters are – create two or three. Write down their names, ages and characteristics, for example, Dwight is 12. He likes football and hates tidying his room.

- Now write down where the scene is set.

- Write the playscript. You do not need many stage directions in a radio play, but you might say how a character should speak his/her lines, for example,

Earl: (*angrily*) **Go upstairs now!**

Keep the scene short and try to keep the tension going.

2 Add a new character to your next scene. S/he should be a stranger who has bad news. How does the family react?

Aim:

~In this homework you will make up a scene from a radio play. You will invent a few characters and write a script for production.~

National Curriculum:

~Speaking and Listening: Range (d) performance of scripted plays~

~Writing: Range (c) playscripts~

Background:

~This homework will help you to improve your ability to write playscripts.~

~ Ask the family ~

Ask members of your family to help you read your scene(s) as if you were on the radio. Each person should take a different role to make the play sound realistic. Record the reading and listen to it together.

Try and sound as sulky as you usually do

stop giving me a hard time

Vocabulary:
playscript
playwright
tension

Spellings:
cannot can't

PUNCHY POETRY 1

Aim:

~In this homework you will consider how words sound and how sound affects meaning. You will find out about alliteration. You will practise reading your words aloud.~

National Curriculum:

~Speaking and Listening: Range (b) adapt presentation to different audiences~
~Writing: Key Skills (b) poetry~
~Writing: Standard English and Language Study (c) imaginative and precise use of words~

Background:

~When alliteration is used two or more words begin with the same letter or sound, e.g. punchy poetry.~

Vocabulary:
alliteration   concise
dictionary   precise

Spellings:
choice   choose   chose

Homework Activity 19

1 Make a list of 20 nouns (people or things) from your home, e.g. television, cat.

• Now add an adjective to describe each noun. The adjective must begin with the same letter or sound as the noun and it must be appropriate. If your cat is friendly, "the cruel cat" may not be appropriate.

So now you might have some words like these:

The cruel cat
My marvellous mum

• Add a verb to the end of each phrase. A verb tells us what the noun is doing, e.g. *The cruel cat cavorts.*

You could look for interesting words in a dictionary or thesaurus.

2 Choose one of the nouns on your list. Write as many alliterations about different qualities of the noun, e.g.

The Cat
Black back begins to bend
Cruel claws caress, etc.

~ Ask the family ~

Talk to someone at home about which words sound best. When your list is complete, read it aloud, trying to make the meaning clear.

PUNCHY POETRY 2

Homework Activity 20

1 Choose a subject that interests you, perhaps something or someone at home, or a place that you know well.

List all the important things about your subject, e.g.

My Gran
old, kind, gives me sweets,
wears a yellow hat,
has sharp eyes.

Now try to write a simile for each fact, e.g.

My Gran
Is old like a well worn book
Gives me sweets like lots of
little rewards for being me

Change any of your words that you do not like.
Write out a neat copy.

2 Consider the subject of stormy weather. Write similes to describe what it is like. Remember to think about all aspects of the subject, e.g. movement, effect of the movement, sounds, etc.

Aim:

~In this homework you will consider how to use similes to make your descriptions more interesting.~

National Curriculum:

~Speaking and Listening: Key Skills (a) use intonation appropriately~

~Writing: Range (a) develop distinctive style~

Background:

~A simile is when you say something is like something else, e.g. "his eyes were like cracked marbles".~

~ Ask the family ~

Read your similes to someone at home. Perhaps together you could think of some similes to describe another member of your family, possibly even yourself.

Vocabulary:
description   simile
subject

Spellings:
disappoint   disappear

21

PUNCHY POETRY 3

Aim:

~ *This homework asks you to consider more ways of creating effective descriptions.* ~

National Curriculum:

~ *AT 3 materials and their Writing: Range (a) develop distinctive style* ~

~ *Writing: Key Skills (b) write poetry* ~

Background:

~ *A metaphor is when something is described as <u>being</u> something else, e.g. The moon is a silver tray, rather than being <u>like</u> something else.* ~

Vocabulary:
detailed   metaphor
effective

Spellings:
describe
description

Homework Activity 21

1 Think of the Sun.

Write ten lines that begin, "The Sun is … ".

Now think of ten different things that the Sun could be described as. Have fun. Think of unusual and interesting ideas. Here are some examples to start you off:

The Sun is a shiny new pound coin

The Sun is a light bulb in the sky

The Sun is a golden dinner plate

The Sun is my happiness

2 Choose another subject and do the same with it. This time, try to make your metaphors longer and more detailed, e.g. My little brother is a happy puppy tearing round the park in circles.

~ Ask the family ~

Ask different people at home to think of metaphors for the Sun, Moon or stars. Write them down with some of your own ideas and create a poem.

Homework Activity 22

Onomatopoeia is when the word you use sounds like what it is describing, e.g. Plop – the stone plopped into the pond.

1 Make a list of all the onomatopoeic words that you can think of.

- After each word, write a description that goes with it, e.g. Thud – the huge wooden doors closed in my face.

  There does not need to be a connection between the ideas that you use for different words.

2 Consider one topic that has lots of interesting onomatopoeias, such as a game or sport, street life or travel. Write a short poem about it using an example of onomatopoeia followed by a description, e.g. Thwack, the bat forced the ball for six.

~ Ask the family ~

See how many onomatopoeic words people at home can come up with. Try to draw a picture to illustrate each word.

Aim:

~In this homework you will think more about how the sound of words suggests meaning in the most obvious way.~

National Curriculum:

~Writing: Range (a) develop distinctive style~
~Writing: Key Skills (b) write poetry~

Background:

~Onomatopoeia is a word that represents a sound, e.g. thud, buzz. Concentrate on actions in order to think of words that suggest that action or sound. Use these words in your descriptions.~

Vocabulary:
action   onomatopoeia
thesaurus

Spellings:
diary   dairy

23

MAKING A DRAMA OUT OF A CRISIS

Aim:

~ You will practise your skills in mime by telling a story through actions not words. ~

National Curriculum:

~ Speaking and Listening: Range (d) participate in drama and consider own performance ~

Background:

~ For this exercise you should not use any props. Be aware of your audience, and make sure that you are communicating the ideas you intend to communicate. ~

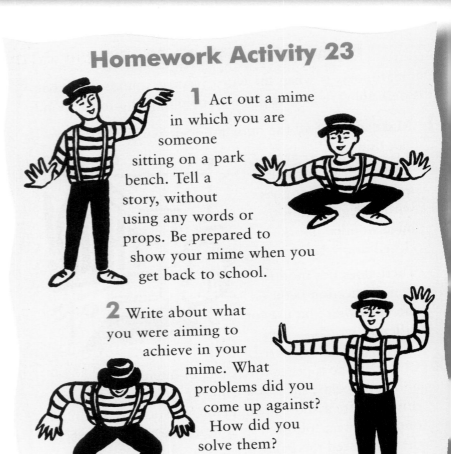

Homework Activity 23

1 Act out a mime in which you are someone sitting on a park bench. Tell a story, without using any words or props. Be prepared to show your mime when you get back to school.

2 Write about what you were aiming to achieve in your mime. What problems did you come up against? How did you solve them?

~ Ask the family ~

Perform your mime to someone at home. Ask your helper what s/he thought of it. Ask your helper to act out the part of a second person who comes to sit on the park bench.

Vocabulary:
communication
mime   review

Spellings:
does   doesn't

Homework Activity 24
~ Ask the family ~

1 For this task, you will need to find someone at home who is willing to work with you.

● Read the following short script together.

A: *Hello.*

B: *Hello.*

A: *What's this?*

B: *What?*

A: *Now stop that.*

B: *I can't.*

● Work out two entirely different ways in which you could act out this scene. Be prepared to talk about them back at school, or to act them out with a friend.

2 Write about your two different interpretations of the script. Try to describe exactly what it is that makes them different.

Aim:

~ *You will need to develop your drama skills, thinking carefully about your actions and your voices.* ~

National Curriculum:

~ *Speaking and Listening: Range (d) participate in scripted play* ~

~ *Reading: Key Skills (a) analyse and discuss alternative interpretations* ~

Background:

~ *This homework will show you that, in a play, a set of words can be given very different meanings according to the way in which they are spoken and presented.* ~

Vocabulary:
interpretation   script

Spellings:
excited   excitement
exciting

Aim:

National Curriculum:

~Speaking and Listening: Range (d) perform scripted plays~

~Writing: Key Skills (b) develop ability to write scripts and dialogue~

Background:

~Playwrights only tell you what the characters do and say. The audience has to make up its own mind about the kind of people the characters are.~

Homework Activity 25

1 Write a speech for one character, in which s/he talks about a happy event in her/his past. Decide who the person is, and what the surroundings are as s/he talks. Learn the speech and be ready to deliver it in your next drama lesson. Do not tell any of your friends who your character is. They will be asked to talk about your character after you have delivered the speech.

2 Create a second character for your play. The character asks, 'So, what's the matter with you now, then?' Write a short conversation between the two characters you have created.

~ Ask the family ~

Discuss your character or characters with someone at home. Your helper may offer suggestions about what to write. If you are doing Task Two, ask someone to act out the scene with you and help you learn your lines.

Vocabulary:
character   dialogue
playwright

Spellings:
except   accept

Homework Activity 26

1 In this short extract from "Romeo and Juliet", a father is angry because his daughter will not marry the man he has chosen for her. He threatens to throw her out of his house if the disobedience continues.

Speak not, reply not, do not answer me!
My fingers itch. Wife, we scarce thought us blest
That God had lent us but this only child;
But now I see this one is one too much,
And that we have a curse in having her.
Thursday is near. Lay hand on heart; advise.
An you be mine, I'll give you to my friend;
An you be not, hang, beg, starve, die in the streets,
For by my soul I'll ne'er acknowledge thee.

Imagine you are the father. Work out how you would speak these lines, and what you would do as you say them. Be ready to talk about this, and to act it out, at school.

2 Imagine that you are the daughter who has been listening to these threats. What would you say in reply? Write your own speech. Be prepared to deliver it at school.

~ Ask the family ~

Show someone at home what you are doing. Ask what your helper thinks of the father. What does s/he think the daughter should do in this situation?

Aim:

~This homework gives you a chance to work with the greatest playwright ever – William Shakespeare!~

National Curriculum: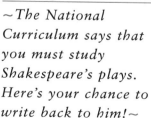

~Speaking and Listening: Range (d) participate in scripted plays~

~Reading: Range (d) plays by Shakespeare~

~Writing: Key Skills (b) develop ability to write scripts~

Background:

~The National Curriculum says that you must study Shakespeare's plays. Here's your chance to write back to him!~

Vocabulary:
disobedience
threaten   acknowledge

Spellings:
final   finally

Aim:

~This homework asks you to look at words and how well they work in different kinds of writing. You will consider who the writer is writing for and the purpose of the text.~

National Curriculum:

~Reading: Standard English and Language Study (a) analyse features of texts~

~ Writing: Range (b) develop thinking through review and analysis~

Background:

~In your reading of texts you should learn to identify the target audience of a piece of writing as well as the purpose for which it is written.~

Vocabulary:

analysis   editorial
purpose   relevant

Spellings:
friend   friendly

Homework Activity 27

1 Find two examples of different kinds of text that appear at home, e.g. a magazine article, a newspaper editorial, a bill, a postcard, an advertisement, a leaflet, etc. For each text answer the following questions:

a) Who is the writer? How can you tell?

b) Who was the text written for? How can you tell?

c) What is the purpose of this text? (Why was it written?) How can you tell?

2 Which of the two texts do you think is the better example of 'good' writing? Paste a section of this text into your homework book and write why you have chosen it.

~ Ask the family ~

Ask someone at home what s/he would consider to be 'good' writing and why. Show your homework to your helper. Perhaps s/he can add some reasons why the text you have chosen is an example of 'good' writing.

Homework Activity 28

1 Read the following description:

The heavy fog hung over the barren moorland. The spongy, green moss was the only sign of the waiting bog. It lay there, sucking in the air gently. A lonely sheep trod warily near the stark grey rocks that stood around the bogland. Quickly, the solitary man ran toward the firm ground near the rocks. He was too confident; the hungry mud swallowed him with deep belches of satisfaction.

- Make a list of all the adjectives that you can find in this text.

- What would the writing be like if you took away the adjectives?

- Why are adjectives used?

2 Make a list of all the verbs that you can find.

- What effect do the verbs have on the extract as a whole?

- How would the writing be changed if you used different verbs?

~ Ask the family ~

Ask someone at home to look at the work with you. Your helper might be able to find some words that you have missed! Talk about the effect of the verbs and adjectives.

Aim:

~This homework asks you to recognise adjectives and verbs as they appear in a piece of writing and to consider how they affect the quality of the writing.~

National Curriculum:

~Reading: Standard English and Language Study (b) characteristics of literary language~

~Writing: Standard English and Language Study (b) grammatical functions of verbs and adjectives~

Background:

~Your own writing will improve if you learn how verbs and adjectives can be used to create effects. An adjective describes a noun, e.g. a _sad_ boy. A verb shows the action.~

Vocabulary:
effect function
verb

Spellings:
fame famous

Aim:

~This homework asks you to think carefully about the use of words within sentences.~

National Curriculum:

~Writing: Standard English and Language Study (b) grammatical functions of words~

Background:

~A writer's choice of words affects not only the mood and atmosphere of the writing but also the meaning of the sentences.~

Homework Activity 29

1 The friendly sun shone … 1 … on the old tiled … 2 … of the village. A … 3 … dog was snuffling in a … 4 … for scraps and walking … 5 … down the street a … 6 … man with a green … 7 … was enjoying the morning … 8 … . Suddenly, a dark-haired woman … 9 … from one of the whitewashed … 10 … shouting loudly in Greek.

- Write down the words that you think would best fill the spaces.

- Can you identify any adjectives in the extract? If so, you will notice that you could put several different words in that space, thus changing the mood of the piece but not its grammatical sense. Now change the adjectives to alter the mood of the writing.

2 Write a short paragraph of your own, missing out every fifth word.

Give it to someone else to complete when you get to school.

Vocabulary:
grammatical   mood

Spellings:
humorous   humour

~ Ask the family ~

Try out your missing words paragraph on someone at home. Which words might your helper have put in the blanks? Discuss the different versions.

THE GLAMOUR OF GRAMMAR 4

Homework Activity 30

1 Re-write these pairs of simple sentences as one compound sentence, using a suitable connective to join the two clauses.

a) I put my coat on. I went for a walk.

b) The lights went out. I was afraid.

c) He was clever. He never did any work.

d) We will not go out today. It is raining.

e) She shut the door. She went into the front room.

Underline the connective in each sentence.

2 Look closely at a paragraph in a book, magazine or paper that you are reading.

● How many sentences are there in the paragraph?

● How many of the sentences are compound?

● Make a list of the connectives which are used in the compound sentences

~ Ask the family ~

Ask someone at home to help you look with Task Two.

Aim:

~To learn how simple sentences can be changed into compound sentences by using connectives such as 'and' or 'but'.~

National Curriculum:

~Writing: Standard English and Language Study (b) principles of sentence grammar~

Background:

~A simple sentence is one that has only one idea or clause, e.g. Tom lives in Ireland. A compound sentence has more than one idea or clause, e.g. I boiled the kettle and made a cup of tea.~

Vocabulary:
connective   compound

Spellings:
high   height

HARD SELL, SOFT SOAP 1

Aim:

~In this homework you will think about the words and images that are used to sell things. You will write down your observations about how the words and images work to persuade the reader to buy.~

National Curriculum:

~Speaking and Listening: Range (a) talk for analysis~

~Reading: Range (e) leaflets~

~Reading: Key Skills (a) engage with language in non-fiction~

Background:

~An adjectives describes a noun, e.g. The <u>huge</u> house. A verb is a word of action, e.g. The teacher <u>coughed</u>.~

Vocabulary:
persuasion
exaggeration

Spellings:
handkerchief
handkerchieves

Homework Activity 31

1 Choose an advertisement from any publication that comes through your letterbox at home. This might be taken from a leaflet, magazine or free newspaper.

FREE! inside

- What are you being persuaded to buy?

- How have images or diagrams been used to persuade you to buy? e.g. There are three small pictures of a cleaning product and one showing a clean floor in an expensive house.

- How has colour been used?

- Write down all the words from the advertisement which you think are used to make you buy the product.

Now BIGGER than ever!

- Is the advertisement good? Why?/Why not?

- Find the adjectives in the advertisement. Write them down.

~ Ask the family ~

Ask different people at home which of the advertisements that come through your letterbox they like/dislike and why. Write down your findings.

HARD SELL, SOFT SOAP 2

Homework Activity 32

1 Write down all the good points about the city, town or village where you live. Now write an advertisement to persuade people to come to your town or village. Make it sound really attractive. Use pictures if you want to.

2 Write down all the bad points about the place where you live. Select those aspects of the area that are not pleasant.

Now write an advertisement to dissuade people from living there.

~ Ask the family ~

Ask someone at home to help you select the right aspects of your area for each task. Ask also for ideas about the best words to use. Do you agree on the good and bad aspects of where you live?

Aim:
~In this homework you will practise your skill using words to persuade.~

National Curriculum:
~Writing: Range (a) variety of purpose~
~Writing: Range (c) advertisements~
~Writing: Key Skills (b) persuasive writing~

Background:
~In this work you must try to persuade others to like or dislike something by the way that you describe it.

Remember: an adjective describes a noun, e.g. The *friendly* giant.~

Vocabulary:
image creation
selection
Spellings:
lonely   loneliness

Aim:

~This homework asks you to use language to persuade, as it would be used in a prepared speech. You will need to convince an imaginary audience of your views.~

National Curriculum:

~Speaking and Listening: Range (a) persuasion~

~Speaking and Listening: Standard English and Language Study: fluent use of Standard English~

Background:

~This work will make you practise the use of Standard English in front of an audience.~

Vocabulary:
bias   tone

Spellings:
opposite
opposition

Homework Activity 33

1 Choose one of the following topics. Write a speech either for or against:

~ loud music ~ foxhunting ~ school uniform ~
~ homework ~ abolishing cars ~ parent power ~

● Make a list of all the reasons for or against. Put them in order, with the most powerful argument last. Now add adjectives and other words that really make your reasons sound convincing.

● Practise reading your speech aloud. Concentrate on looking at your audience, pausing when you say something good and saying important things loudly.

2 Add some comments that are against your own viewpoint. Argue against them proving that your view is better.

~ Ask the family ~

Ask someone at home to listen to your speech and to suggest ways of improving it. Make sure that you look at your audience when you give your speech. Try to sound like other public speakers who you may have seen on television.

HARD SELL, SOFT SOAP 4

Homework Activity 34

1 Watch a television advertisement. Answer the following questions about the advertisement:

- What is the name of the product advertised?
- What made you notice the name of the product?
- What do you hear? Include music, words and sound effects.
- How is the sound used to try to sell the product?
- Describe, in detail, what you can see, e.g. There is a young woman washing up and smiling. It is sunny, etc.
- How does what you see help to sell the product?

2 Decide on a product to advertise. This might be a product that already exists or one that you have made up.

Draw six frames like the ones above. In them draw the images for the beginning of the advertisement. (see *Ask the family*).

~ **Ask the family** ~

Ask someone at home to look at your work. Perhaps s/he might help you plan the images. Talk about which images and sounds would work best.

Aim:

~In this homework you will look at a television advertisement and write about how it is trying to sell the product that it is advertising. You will also plan the beginning of an advertisement of your own.~

National Curriculum:

~Reading: Range (f) television~

~Reading: Standard English and Language Study (b) language in the media~

~Writing: Range (c) advertisements~

Background:

~It is important to become a critical reader of media texts, including television advertisements, and to learn to identify the different persuasive techniques used.~

Vocabulary:
audience   product

Spellings:
luscious   luxurious

35

Aim:

~You will try your hand at writing definitions of words, just like the most famous writer of a dictionary, Samuel Johnson.~

National Curriculum:

~Reading: Range (e) read wide range of non-fiction texts~

Background:

~Samuel Johnson lived from 1709 to 1784. In 1755, he published "A Dictionary of the English Language". It was the first major attempt to organise the English language in this way. Johnson wrote definitions for over 40,000 words.~

Homework Activity 35

Samuel Johnson lived from 1709 to 1784.

1 Read these definitions that Johnson wrote:

tadpole A young shapeless frog or toad, consisting only of a body and a tail; a porwiggle.

tarantula An insect whose bite is only cured by music.

tree A large vegetable rising, with one large woody stem, to a considerable height.

Now try writing three definitions of your own of everyday creatures or plants.

2 See if you can improve on Johnson's definitions of a tadpole, a tarantula and a tree. Write your own definitions.

Vocabulary:
definition text dictionary

Spellings:
pay paid

~ Ask the family ~

Read Johnson's definitions to someone at home, without telling your helper the word which is being defined!

Try out your own definitions in the same way. Think of words which are important to you both and decide on your own definitions.

Homework Activity 36

1 Read this extract from Pepys's diary:

2 September 1666

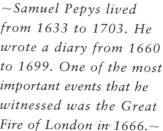

Everybody endeavouring to remove their goods, and flinging into the river or bringing them into lighters that lay off. Poor people staying in their houses as long as till the very fire touched them, and then running into boats or clambering from one pair of stairs by the waterside to another. And among other things, the poor pigeons I perceive were loath to leave their house, but hovered about the windows and balconies till they were some of them burned, their wings, and fell down. At last met my Lord Mayor in Canning Street, like a man spent, with a hankercher about his neck. He cried like a fainting woman, "Lord, what can I do? I am spent! People will not obey me. I have been pulling down houses. But the fire overtakes us faster than we can do it."

Watch a news story on television or read one from a newspaper. Imagine that you are a witness to that important event. Write your account of what it was like to be there. Try to put in lots of detail, as Pepys does when he describes the pigeons.

2 Continue Pepys's account. Write as if you were also at the Great Fire of London. Try to make your writing similar to his.

~ Ask the family ~

Ask someone at home to recall an important event. Try to use the information and feelings which s/he has given you in your writing.

Aim:

~In this homework you will try your hand at writing a report of a major event.~

National Curriculum:

~Speaking and Listening: Range (c) listen attentively~

~Reading: Range (e) wide range of non-fiction~

~Writing: Range (c) write reports~

Background:

~Samuel Pepys lived from 1633 to 1703. He wrote a diary from 1660 to 1699. One of the most important events that he witnessed was the Great Fire of London in 1666.~

Vocabulary:
diary witness

Spellings:
lay lie lie
laid lied lay

Aim:

~ *You will write like a scientist, observing a piece of behaviour very closely.* ~

National Curriculum:

~ *Writing: Range (c) write reports* ~

Background:

~ *Charles Darwin lived from 1809 to 1882. He was the first scientist to write publicly about the theory of evolution. The writing in this extract comes from his book "On the Origin of Species by means of Natural Selection". He is describing what he means by instinctive behaviour in animals.* ~

Vocabulary:

behaviour   instinct
species

Spellings:

poem   poetry

Homework Activity 37

1 Read this extract from Darwin's "Origin of Species":

But let us look to the familiar case of the several breeds of dogs: it cannot be doubted that young pointers (I have myself seen a striking instance) will sometimes point and even back other dogs the very first time they are taken out; retrieving is certainly in some degree inherited by retrievers; and a tendency to run round, instead of at, a flock of sheep, by shepherd dogs. I cannot see that these actions, performed without experience by the young and in nearly the same manner by each individual, performed with eager delight by each breed, and without the end being known, – for the young pointer can no more know that he points to aid his master, than the white butterfly knows why she lays her eggs on the leaf of the cabbage, – I cannot see that these actions differ essentially from true instincts.

Now write, as if you were a scientist, about some behaviour which you have observed either in an animal or in a very young child.

2 Have you noticed any behaviour in an animal or a young child that you would call instinctive? Write in detail about one example.

~ Ask the family ~

Ask someone at home whether s/he has noticed any example of behaviour in an animal or young child which your helper would call instinctive.

Homework Activity 38

1 Read the following extract from Dorothy Wordsworth's journal:

I never saw daffodils so beautiful they grew among the mossy stones about and about them, some rested their heads upon these stones as on a pillow for weariness and the rest tossed and reeled and danced and seemed as if they verily laughed with the wind that blew upon them over the lake, they looked so gay ever glancing ever changing.

Look closely at something in nature; it may be the sky, some trees, flowers. Write about it in precise detail. Your writing need not be very long, but it should be detailed, and show that you have spent some time observing.

2 Dorothy Wordsworth uses metaphors in her description: she compares the daffodils to people, resting their heads on pillows, dancing and laughing. Use some metaphors in your writing.

Aim:

~In this homework you are asked to write about something in nature which you have observed very carefully.~

National Curriculum:

~Reading: Range (e) wide range of non-fiction~

Writing: Range (c) write reports~

Background:

~Dorothy Wordsworth lived from 1771 to 1855. She kept many journals throughout her life. The extract here comes from her "Grasmere Journal" which she wrote in the years 1800 to 1803.~

~ Ask the family ~

Talk to someone at home about what they like about nature, then ask your helper to come out with you to observe something very carefully. Read out what you wrote, but leave out the name of what you are observing. See how long it takes your helper to guess correctly what it is.

Vocabulary:
journal   metaphor
Spellings:
quite   quiet

~In this homework you are asked to write about something that annoys or upsets you.~

National Curriculum:

~Speaking and Listening: Range (c) listen attentively~

~Reading: Range (e) wide range of non-fiction~

~Writing: Range (c) write reports~

Homework Activity 39

1 Read this extract from Elizabeth Fry's prose:

I have just returned from a most melancholy visit to Newgate, where I have been at the request of Elizabeth Fricker, previous to her execution tomorrow morning, at eight o'clock. I found her much hurried, distressed, and tormented in mind. Her hands cold, and covered with something like the perspiration preceding death, and in an universal tremor ... Besides this poor young woman, there are also six men to be hanged, one of whom has a wife near her confinement, also condemned, and seven young children. Since the awful report came down, he has become quite mad, from horror of mind. A strait waistcoat could not keep him within bounds: he had just bitten the turnkey; I saw the man come out with his hand bleeding, as I passed the cell.

Vocabulary:
campaigner   reformer
significant

Spellings:
receipt   receive

2 Write about something you have heard that has annoyed or upset you, and which you would like to see changed.

Notice how Elizabeth Fry does not write too much about how terrible hanging is, but tries to influence her reader with small but significant details.

Try to do this in your writing.

Background:

~ Elizabeth Fry was a Quaker who was keen to improve the conditions in which the poor were living. In 1817 she began a prison reform society to campaign for changes in the prison system.

The penal code in England in the early part of the nineteenth century was very savage. More than 200 offences were punishable by death, including minor theft, housebreaking, sheepstealing and forgery, and it was not unknown for young children to be hanged for stealing a loaf of bread. ~

~ Ask the family ~

Ask people at home what really annoys and upsets them, which they would like to see changed. Try to use their ideas in your writing.

**Aim:**

~In this homework you
will write something to
yourself! You will open
it and read it again in
several years' time.~

National
Curriculum:

~Reading: Range (e)
wide range of non-
fiction~

~Writing: Range (c)
write personal letter~

Vocabulary:
parlour

Spellings:
rhythm   rhyme

Homework Activity 40

1 Read Emily Bronte's diary paper:

*I fed Rainbow, Diamond, Snowflake Jasper phesant
… Taby said just now come Anne pillopatate (ie pill
a potato) Aunt has come into the Kitchen just now
and said where are your feet Anne Anne answered
on the floor Aunt papa opened the parlour door and
gave Branwell a Letter saying here Branwell read
this and show it to your Aunt and Charlotte – The
Gondals are discovering the interior of Gaaldine …*

*It is past Twelve o'clock Anne and I have not tidied
ourselves, done our bed work or done our lessons
and we want to go out to play … Taby said on my
putting a pen in her face Ya pitter pottering there
insted of pilling a potate I answered O Dear, O
Dear, O Dear I will derictly with that I get up, take
a Knife and begin pilling …*

*Anne and I say I wonder what we shall be like (if all
be well) and what we shall be and where we shall be
if all goes on well in the year 1874 - in which year I
shall be in my 57th year Anne will be going in her
55th year Branwell will be going in his 58th year
And Charlotte in her 59th year hoping we shall all
be well at that time We close our paper*

Emily and Anne November the 24 1834

2 Write something about yourself to yourself. Decide where you will put it for safety, and when in the future you will re-read it – in ten years time, twenty years time. You do not have to bring your writing to school; it is a personal exercise.

Background:

~Emily Bronte lived from 1818 to 1848. She wrote the diary paper, when she was 16 years old, on a scrap of paper less than 10cm by 6cm. It was found folded up tightly in a small box, after her death. She intended to open it when she was 57: she died of consumption when she was 29.

Her novel "Wuthering Heights" is generally considered among the greatest in the English language. ~

~ Ask the family ~

Do you know if anyone else in the family has done something similar to this?

Read Emily Bronte's diary paper to someone at home. If you want to, tell someone what you are planning to do. But the real audience for this piece of writing is your future self.

Aim:

~This homework asks you to think about how comic strip characters attract readers and how comic strip stories work.~

National Curriculum:

~Reading: Range (f) media with different structural devices~

Background:

~It is important to realise that the comic strips that you enjoy have been carefully crafted by someone. This homework asks you to analyse a successful example of this kind of publication.~

Vocabulary:
target audience

Spellings:
stop   stopped

Homework Activity 41

1 Select your favourite comic strip character. This might be a character from your reading as a child, or from your reading now.

- Cut out an example of one frame of a story that shows your chosen character and stick it into your exercise book.

- Explain why you have chosen this character. What is it about the character that appeals to you?

  You might describe what s/he looks like, how s/he behaves or what happens to her/him in the stories.

2 Write an analysis of the comic from which your character is taken. How many stories does the comic have? What kind of stories are they? What else is in the comic? What is the target audience for this comic?

~ Ask the family ~

Find out which comics members of your family used to read. What was the appeal of these comics? Compare them with the comics that you have read.

Homework Activity 42

1 Remind yourself of one of your favourite childhood stories. Choose six significant moments in the story.

● For each moment, draw a comic strip frame picture and add words.

The words could be written in speech bubbles or in a small box underneath the picture.

You should now have a six-picture comic strip that tells the story.

2 Now try to add a twist to the plot. Choose frame number two, three or four and change the last few pictures so that the story takes on a new meaning.

Sleeping Beauty woke up with a start

Who was it kissing her?

She realised it was that horrible prince

~ Ask the family ~

Ask someone at home to read both of your comic strips. Which does s/he prefer and why?

Aim:
~This homework asks you to plan and present a story in comic strip form.~

National Curriculum:
~Writing: Range (b) aesthetic and imaginative purposes~

Background:
~Homework Activity 41 asked you to reflect on aspects of comic strip writing. This time you will create your own comic strip so that you can put a different slant on a well-known story.~

Vocabulary:
frame   form

Spellings:
surprise   surprising

COMICS AND MAGAZINES 3

Aim:

~In this homework you are asked to analyse and engage with the ideas, themes and language of magazine writing. You will need to write down your findings clearly.~

National Curriculum:

~Reading: Key Skills (a) ideas, themes and language in non-fiction~

~Writing: Range (c) reviews~

Background:

~You need wide reading experience and an awareness of how texts written for different audiences use different language and style.~

Vocabulary:
review   paragraph

Spellings:
sincere   sincerely

Homework Activity 43

1 Select your favourite magazine. Write down the title of the magazine. Write full answers to the following questions:

a) What kind of people do you think would read this magazine?

b) What age range is it aimed at?

c) Look at the contents page. Write a brief list of the kinds of topics that the magazine is about.

d) Is most of the space given to writing or to pictures?

e) Is the language used difficult or easy to understand? Give examples.

f) Why do you like the magazine?

2 Write up your answers as a continuous piece of writing that might appear as a review of the magazine. Add any other appropriate comments. Remember to use suitable paragraphs and punctuation.

~ Ask the family ~

Ask someone at home which magazines s/he reads. What does your helper enjoy about them? Ask the questions above and make notes on the answers.

Homework Activity 44

1 Choose a subject that you would expect to find in your favourite magazine.

- Now plan an article on that subject. You might have to make up things such as interviews with famous people or accounts of visits you may have made. You are trying to appeal to the people who read the magazine regularly.

- When you have written your first draft, compare your work with an article from the magazine. Use words that are similar to other articles. You may need to change parts of your writing at this point so that you use the house style of the magazine. (See *Ask the family*.)

- Now write up the final draft in paragraphs, taking care with punctuation.

~ Ask the family ~

Ask some people at home to read through your article and to compare it with articles in the magazine. What do they think?

Can they suggest any changes to your writing to make it more like the magazine's style?

Aim:

~This homework builds on Homework Activity 43. This time you will use your knowledge of the style of the magazine to write an article that could appear in it.~

National Curriculum:

~Writing: Range (b) writing for specific readers~

Background:

~It is important to learn to write for specific readers. This homework asks you to apply the analysis of a magazine to the task of writing for that magazine in an appropriate style.~

Vocabulary:
house style   reflection

Spellings:
could   should   would

Aim:

~This homework asks you to watch and think about a soap opera in order to develop your analytical skills.~

National Curriculum:

~Reading: Range (f) analysing television~

Background:

~You need to develop a critical ability in relation to all forms of media as well as all forms of written texts.~

Homework Activity 45

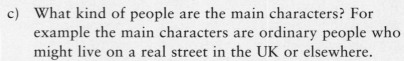

1 Watch an episode of a soap opera. Before you do so, read the following questions so that you know what to look for when you watch the programme.

a) What is the name of the soap opera?

b) Describe the setting, e.g. most of the scenes take place in a pub, or in people's houses.

c) What kind of people are the main characters? For example the main characters are ordinary people who might live on a real street in the UK or elsewhere.

d) Describe one character in detail, including age, gender and what has happened to her/him in the episode.

e) Write a brief account of the main things that happened in the episode.

2 Design a poster advertising the soap opera you have watched. Think about how to excite and interest potential viewers.

Vocabulary:
potential episode
critical

Spellings:
tried try

~ Ask the family ~

Which soap operas do your family watch?
Why do they like them? Are there some things which
they do not enjoy about the programmes?
Write up your findings.

SOAP SPRINGS ETERNAL 2

Homework Activity 46

1 Think of a character in a soap opera that you watch. Decide what will happen to that character in the next few weeks and months of the programme. Consider how the character will behave, what kinds of setting the action will take place in and how other characters will react. Write down your ideas clearly, taking care with spelling and punctuation.

2 Write notes for one episode of your storyline, e.g. two women have been arguing over a man. Woman 1 walks down a dark street. She carries something. Camera close-up to a spray paint can. Cut to shot of Woman 2's car covered with paint graffiti. Next shot shows the two women arguing about who caused the damage, etc.

~ Ask the family ~

Read your ideas for a storyline to someone at home. Talk to your helper about how realistic the ideas are. Add any new ideas that you discuss.

Aim:

~In this homework you are asked to create a new storyline for a character in a soap opera that you watch.~

National Curriculum:

~Reading: Key Skills (b) reflect on presentation of ideas, motivation and behaviour of characters~
~Writing: Range (b) narration~

Background:

~A storyline in a soap opera or drama will set down what is going to happen to a character. You will not need to write descriptions but you do have to say, in detail, what you see that character doing.~

Vocabulary:
storyline graffiti
Spellings:
wonder wonderful

49

Aim:

~This homework asks you to build on the work done in Homework Activities 45 and 46. Here you will create an entirely new soap opera with your own characters and setting.~

National Curriculum:

~Writing: Key Skills (b) use knowledge of story structure and means of conveying relationships~

Background:

~It is important that you learn to apply your own creative ideas to your knowledge of how soap operas are put together. You will need to think about character, setting and storyline.~

Vocabulary:
convey
circumstances

Spellings:
write   writing

Homework Activity 47

1 Decide on a setting for a new soap opera. It might be in a country area or in a city or town, but it must be based around a place where people live.

It must involve all sorts and ages of people, who may also be from different cultures.

● Describe this place.

● Now write about four or five main characters. Consider the age, gender, culture, likes and dislikes, and circumstances, e.g. Are they married? etc.

2 Write a brief storyline for each of your characters that would be included in the first few episodes.

~ Ask the family ~

Show your homework to someone at home. Ask your helper to consider your soap opera plans. Perhaps s/he can suggest some changes or details to add.

Homework Activity 48

1 Using one or more of the storylines that you created in Homework Activity 47, write the playscript for one scene of one episode. It does not have to be the first episode but you may need to set the scene briefly before you begin, e.g. the two characters, Bill and Ben, are sitting outside a pub in summer talking about Bill's wife.

- Write out the scene in full as a playscript, e.g.

  Bill: She's not happy, you know.

  Ben: Why not, Bill? Don't you give her any time?

- Don't forget to add directions for the actors, e.g.

  Bill stands up and hits Ben.

- Try to make the speech and the directions for the actors interesting for an audience. Remember that lots of things happen in a soap opera. Enjoy it!

~ Ask the family ~

Why not ask someone at home to help you try out your scene, to help you read it aloud? Does it sound good? What does your helper think?

Aim:

~In this homework you will complete the series on soap operas by writing the script for one scene of the soap opera that you invented in Homework Activity 47.~

National Curriculum:

~Writing: Range (c) playscript~

~Writing: Key Skills (b) develop knowledge of structure, setting, plot and character~

Background:

~This homework puts together your knowledge of how soap operas are constructed and develops your skill of narration (telling a story) in a specific context, for a specific audience.~

Vocabulary:
believable
appropriate

Spellings:
weather   whether

HELLO, SHAKESPEARE 1

Aim:

~You will have the chance to enjoy Shakespeare's language and to think about the images which words can create in your imagination.~

National Curriculum:

~Speaking and Listening: Range (d) perform scripted plays~

Background:

~The lines in this homework come from the play "King Lear". Lear is an old man, and has done some foolish things in his life. He has come to realise his mistakes, as he stands in the middle of a storm.~

```
Vocabulary:
image   imagination
Spellings:
accommodate
accommodation
```

Homework Activity 49

1 Read these lines from "King Lear":

> *Blow winds, and crack your cheeks; rage, blow*
> *You cataracts, and hurricanes spout,*
> *Till you have drench'd our steeples, drown'd the cocks.*
> *You sulphurous and thought-executing fires,*
> *Vaunt-couriers of oak-cleaving thunderbolts,*
> *Singe my white head. And thou all-shaking thunder,*
> *Strike flat the thick rotundity o' th' world,*
> *Crack Nature's moulds, all germens spill at once*
> *That makes ungrateful man.*

Read these lines aloud at home several times. Shout them out and whisper them. Explain to everyone at home that you have not gone mad. Choose a particular line which you especially like and memorise it. Be prepared to say it aloud at school.

2 Choose one image which these lines create. Draw a picture of the image. Write down the words that make up that image and write about why you have chosen it.

~ Ask the family ~

Persuade someone at home to join you in speaking these lines out loud. Ask your helper what images come to mind.

Homework Activity 50

1 Read these words taken from the first scene of "The Tempest":

> *We run ourselves aground.*
> *Bestir, bestir.*
> *Take in the topsail.*
> *Tend to the master's whistle.*
> *Blow till thou burst thy wind.*
> *I pray now keep below. Keep your cabins.*
> *Down with the topmast.*
> *All lost, to prayers, to prayers! All lost!*
> *We split, we split - Farewell my wife and children -*
> *Farewell brother - We split, we split, we split.*

- Now write down answers to these questions. Who do you think is speaking each line? What is happening as each line is spoken?

- Draw some pictures that some of the lines suggest.

2 Be ready to direct some of your friends in the scene when you get back to school. Write some notes about how they should speak and move when they perform the scene.

Aim:

~You will use Shakespeare's words as clues to the actions that he wanted his actors to perform as they spoke the words.~

National Curriculum:

~Speaking and Listening: Range (d) perform scripted plays~

Background:

~Shakespeare's play "The Tempest" begins with a shipwreck. People on board the ship speak the words you are about to read.~

~ Ask the family ~

Ask someone at home to listen to the lines. Ask for suggestions for your drawings and stage directions.

Vocabulary:
direct   perform
scene

Spellings:
appal   appalling

HELLO, SHAKESPEARE 3

Aim:

~In this homework you will work out the clues which Shakespeare provides in a speech to determine the personality of the character who is speaking.~

National Curriculum:

~Speaking and Listening: Range (d) perform scripted plays~

Background:

~At the beginning of "Richard the Third", Richard explains why he feels like an outcast from society, and why he wants to pay the world back by doing evil deeds.~

Homework Activity 51

1 Read the following extract from "Richard the Third":

> But I, that am not shaped for sportive tricks,
> Nor made to court an amorous looking-glass;
> I, that am rudely stamped, and want love's majesty
> To strut before a wanton ambling nymph;
> I, that am curtailed of this fair proportion,
> Cheated of feature by dissembling Nature,
> Deformed, unfinished, sent before my time
> Into this breathing world, scarce half made up, ...
> And that so lamely and unfashionable
> That dogs bark at me as I halt by them;
> I am determined to prove a villain
> And hate the idle pleasures of these days.

Read these lines aloud many times, then draw a picture of the image which stays most clearly in your mind.

2 Write down in your own words what Richard is saying. Turn your own words into a speech. Say them aloud several times.

~ Ask the family ~

Ask someone at home to listen to you as you speak these words. Ask your helper to join in, and show you a different way of reading them. Experiment with different voices and different volumes. Enjoy yourselves!

Vocabulary:
character image
personality

Spellings:
anxious anxiety

Homework Activity 52

1 Read this argument which Petruchio and Katherina have when they first meet:

P: *Myself am moved to woo thee for my wife.*

K: *"Moved" - in good time! Let him that moved you hither*
Remove you hence. I knew you at the first
You were a movable.

P: *Why, what's a movable?*

K: *A joint stool.*

P: *Thou hast hit it. Come sit on me.*

K: *Asses are made to bear, and so are you.*

P: *Women are made to bear, and so are you.*

K: *No such jade as you, if me you mean.*

P: *Alas, good Kate, I will not burden thee,*
For, knowing thee to be but young and light -

K: *Too light for such a swain as you to catch,*
And yet as heavy as my weight should be …

P: *Come, come, you wasp! I'faith you are too angry.*

K: *If I be waspish, best beware my sting.*

Think of an action to fit with each speech. Write down what the actions should be.

2 Imagine you are Petruchio. Write a paragraph describing your first impressions of Katherina. Now imagine that you are Katherina, and write about Petruchio.

~ Ask the family ~

Ask someone at home to act out the scene with you. Try to be as imaginative as you can when you decide on the movements you will make as you perform the words.

Aim:

~*In this homework you will see how Shakespeare stages an argument between two characters. You will have to make some decisions about staging, and about the personalities of the characters involved.*~

National Curriculum:

~*Speaking and Listening: Range (d) perform scripted plays*~

Background:

~*In "The Taming of the Shrew", Petruchio and Katherina have many arguments, but they eventually marry.*~

Vocabulary:
shrew   staging

Spellings:
apologise
apologize apology

Aim:

~ *In this homework you will look at the work of a writer with a very distinctive style, deciding what the main features of that style are, and then attempting to imitate it.* ~

National Curriculum:

~ *Reading: Range (c) read texts from other cultures and traditions* ~

~ *Writing: Key Skills (b) develop ability to write scripts* ~

Homework Activity 53

1 Read the following extract from Dylan Thomas's "Under Milk Wood":

FIRST VOICE

The sunny slow lulling afternoon yawns and moons through the dozy town. The sea lolls, laps and idles in, with fishes sleeping in its lap. The meadows still as Sunday, the shut-eye tasselled bulls, the goat-and-daisy dingles, nap happy and lazy. The dumb duck-ponds snooze. Clouds sag and pillow on Llareggub Hill. Pigs grunt in a wet wallow-bath, and smile as they snort and dream. They dream of the acorned swill of the world, the rooting for pig-fruit, the bagpipe dugs of the mother sow, the squeal and snuffle of yesses of the women pigs in rut. They mud-bask and snout in the pig-loving sun; their tails curl; they rollick and slobber and snore to deep, smug after-swill sleep. Donkeys angelically drowse on Donkey Down.

MRS PUGH	*Persons with manners,*
SECOND VOICE	*snaps Mrs cold Pugh*
MRS PUGH	*do not nod at table.*
FIRST VOICE	*Mr Pugh cringes awake …*
MRS PUGH	*You should wait until you retire to your sty,*
SECOND VOICE	*says Mrs Pugh, sweet as a razor.*

Read the extract several times with people at home playing some of the parts. Think about how the words should be read aloud. Think about the accents, the tone, the volume and the contrasts of the different voices. Be ready to speak this extract aloud at school.

2 Look at the way Dylan Thomas creates his picture of a sleepy, sunny afternoon, then breaks that atmosphere when the characters begin to speak. Notice the onomatopoeia, the alliteration, the vocabulary, the lists, the way in which he creates new words by linking with a hyphen.

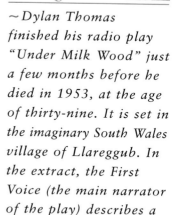

- Find examples of each of these and write them down.

- Write a few Thomas-type sentences of your own, on the theme of evening in your home village, town or city.

Background:

~ *Dylan Thomas finished his radio play "Under Milk Wood" just a few months before he died in 1953, at the age of thirty-nine. It is set in the imaginary South Wales village of Llareggub. In the extract, the First Voice (the main narrator of the play) describes a sunny afternoon.*

Alliteration is explained in Homework 19, and in the glossary.

Onomatopoeia is explained in Homework 22, and in the glossary. ~

~ Ask the family ~

Ask someone at home to help you with the reading of the extract. Ask for ideas which will help you with Task Two. Read what you have written, and ask for suggestions about how to improve it.

Vocabulary:
contrast   volume

Spellings:
advertise
advertisement

Aim:

~ In this homework you will look at the way in which a writer describes an event that happened in his past, when he was living in a different country. You will have a go at this kind of writing yourself. ~

Homework Activity 54

1 Read the following extract from "Home is here now":

I was only twelve years old, and so was she. (I know that sounds very young, but back then people in China got married a lot sooner than they do now. I knew boys who were only thirteen or fourteen, yet already had children of their own.) The girl I once loved would go down to the river every morning and scoop out two buckets of water for her family to use, and she would pass by our house on her way back home even though it was out of her way. I used to sit by my bedroom window and wait for her. And when I leaned out the window and asked her if she needed any help, she would wrinkle up her nose at me and say, "What good can you do, turnip head?"

I didn't even know her name. I thought the two of us could carry on like this forever, and that our little exchanges were something we would end up telling our children and grandchildren about. That girl, that sixty-four-year-old woman, is probably still in China. Maybe she's still living in Danpeng, with a man I can only imagine. I left China at the age of fourteen, when a Catholic missionary sponsored my passage to America. I haven't been back since. Home is here now.

DIFFERENT VOICES 2

- Think about a time in the past when something important happened to you in a place which is not your home now. Write about it. If you do not want to write about yourself, ask someone at home for one of their memories and write about that.

2 Notice how David Xiao builds up the first paragraph, so that you expect something romantic to happen, then destroys that atmosphere when the girl says something rude to him. Notice also how he ends on a note of sadness or nostalgia. Use these two techniques in your own writing: the build-up and knock-down; the sadness or nostalgia.

Background:

~David Xiao, who wrote the article "Home is here now", was born in Hong Kong and now lives in Seattle, USA.~

~ Ask the family ~

Ask someone at home for a memory from their past when they lived somewhere else. Are the memories tinged with sadness, like David Xiao's? When you have written your piece, ask your helper for comments and suggestions.

Vocabulary:
build-up   nostalgia

Spellings:
analyse   analysis

Homework Activity 55

1 Read the following extract from "Quelques Fleurs
(A Tale of Two Sisters)":

*His Mother's a problem. Always hus been. I don't
know what she wants. Take last year, racked my
brains, no help from Him as per usual, left to Him
we'd end up getting a bottle of Bailey's, a gift voucher
and a peeted lip all through the Christmas dinner!
Anyway I done my best, lovely wee lambswool cardi,
sortofa mauveish, a blueish mauvey no pinkish,
nothing too roary, not my taste but then I'm not
seventy-four in February. Gorgeous, but. Self-covered
buttons. Scotch Wool Shop as well, none of your
made-in-Hong-Kongs. So. I goes into the top drawer
of her tallboy looking for clean guest towels for her
toilet and there it is. Still done up in the blinking
glitterwrap the following November! Says she's
keeping it for a special occasion.
I felt like saying where do you
think you're going, your
age, crippled with
arthritis? But I bit
my tongue.*

- This piece is written to be spoken aloud in a Scottish accent. Try to read it in a Scottish accent at home! Ask someone to listen to you, or to help you.

- Now try to write something which can be spoken in your own accent. Make it sound as much as possible like you having a talk with a friend.

Background:

~Liz Lochhead was born in Motherwell, Lanarkshire, Scotland. She now lives in Glasgow.

The word 'non-standard' is defined in the glossary.~

2 Pick out and write down all the non-standard spellings, expressions and sentence constructions in Liz Lochhead's writing. Rewrite the passage, as though it was spoken by some people you know. Think about their accent and their ways of expressing themselves.

~ **Ask the family** ~

People at home can be tremendously useful to you in this homework. You will need to listen carefully to the way people speak, and ask for their help as you try to write it down as accurately as you can.

Vocabulary:
accent   construction
non-standard

Spellings:
caution   cautious

Homework Activity 56

1 Read this poem by Benjamin Zephaniah.

"Vegan Delight"

Ackees, chapatties
Dumplins an nan,
Channa an rotis
Onion uttapam,
Masala dosa
Green callaloo
Bhel an samosa
Corn an aloo
Yam an cassava
Pepperpot stew,
Rotlo an guava
Rice an tofu,
Puri, paratha
Sesame casserole,
Brown eggless pasta
An brown bread rolls

Soya milked muesli
Soya bean curd,
Soya sweet sweeties
Soya's de word,
Soya bean margarine
Soya bean sauce,
What can mek medicine?
Soya of course

Soya meks yoghurt
Soya ice-cream,
Or soya sorbet
Soya reigns supreme,
Soya sticks liquoriced
Soya salads
Try any soya dish
Soya is bad.

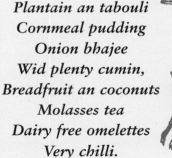

Plantain an tabouli
Cornmeal pudding
Onion bhajee
Wid plenty cumin,
Breadfruit an coconuts
Molasses tea
Dairy free omelettes
Very chilli.

Ginger bread, nut roast
Sorrell, paw paw,
Cocoa an rye toast
I tek dem on tour,
Drinking cool maubi
Meks me feel sweet,
What was that question now?
What do we eat?

● Imagine that you are a poet on tour, and you have chosen to perform this poem. Be prepared to read it out at school.

2 Write a poem about the food you eat. Try to make it sound as appetising as Benjamin Zephaniah's vegan food.

Background:

~Benjamin Zephaniah writes in the introduction to the book from which this poem is taken:

"I write poems for you And I hope that one day You will write poems for me. Read on and write soon." ~

~ Ask the family ~

Ask a few people at home what they feel about vegetarianism and veganism. Ask them to help you to compile an appetising list of the food you eat at home.

Vocabulary:
appetising vegan
vegetarian

Spellings:
courage courageous

Aim:

~ *In this homework you will respond to a poem by thinking about its theme and by writing poems of your own.~*

National Curriculum:

~ *Reading: Range (c) read texts from other cultures and traditions~*

~ *Writing: Range (b) writing to develop thinking~*

Homework Activity 57

1 Read the poem "The Sari":

Inside my mother
I peered through a glass porthole.
The world beyond was hot and brown.
They were all looking in on me

Father, Grandmother,
the cook's boy, the sweeper-girl,
the bullock with the sharp
shoulderblades,
the local politicians.

My English grandmother
took a telescope
and gazed across continents.

All the people unravelled a sari.
It stretched from Lahore to Hyderabad,
wavered across the Arabian Sea,
shot through with stars,
fluttering with sparrows and quails.
They threaded it with roads,
undulations of land.

Eventually
they wrapped and wrapped me in it
whispering Your body is your country.

- Imagine, like Moniza Alvi, that you could have looked out of your mother's womb and seen the people and animals around you. Who would have been there? Who would have been looking on from a long distance away, like Moniza Alvi's English grandmother? What would they have wrapped you in? What would they have whispered to you? Discuss your answers with someone at home.

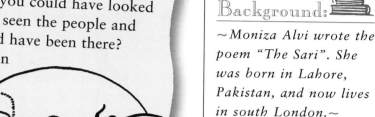

Background:

~Moniza Alvi wrote the poem "The Sari". She was born in Lahore, Pakistan, and now lives in south London.~

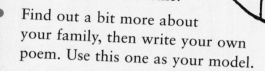

- Find out a bit more about your family, then write your own poem. Use this one as your model.

2 Think about one particular member of your family. Find out as much about her/him as you can. Picture her/him in a certain place. Write a poem that describes the place, what the person looks like, what s/he is doing and what s/he is saying.

~ Ask the family ~

Talk to someone at home about your family, those who are close by and those who are far away. Write about what you find out in a poetic way.

Vocabulary:
poetic   respond
theme

Spellings:
conscious
consciousness

Aim:

~ *This homework asks you to look at a piece of autobiographical writing and to identify the things about it that make it a successful example of this kind of text.* ~

National Curriculum:

~ *Reading: Range (e) autobiography* ~

~ *Writing: Range (c) autobiography* ~

Background

~ *Autobiography allows the reader to see life through one particular person's eyes. The readers feel that they are invited to share the experience that the writer has lived through.* ~

Vocabulary:
congealed   confident

Spellings:
conscience
conscientious

Homework Activity 58

1 Read the following:

BREAKFAST TIME AT BOARDING SCHOOL.

I look at my congealed baked beans and greasy bacon. I must eat it quickly. It is nearly eight o'clock. I pass the salt to the prefect at the end of my table. Will I ever have breasts and look as beautiful and confident as her? I lift my fork to eat; too late. The news has started. We must sit in silence and listen to the radio. The voice drones on loudly in the packed but strangely quiet hall. There are paintings of school governors all around the walls. I study them. What old men they are! Why are there no women? The bell rings for the end of breakfast. We file out.

Answer the following questions:

● What do you notice about the length of the sentences? What is the effect of this?

● How can you tell that the writer is unhappy?

2 Write a paragraph about a time when you were unhappy.

~ **Ask the family** ~

Ask members of your family to tell you about a time when they were unhappy as children. How was the unhappiness overcome? Compare this to your own experience.

Homework Activity 59

1 Choose a memory from your past. It might be a time when you were very sad or perhaps very happy. You might want to write about your first day at school or about an argument with your friends. It doesn't matter what you write about as long as you are happy to let your teacher read it.

- Now try to write about that memory as if you were re-living it. Your reader should be able to see what you see, hear what you hear and feel as you felt. It might be useful to start with a list of adjectives and verbs, e.g. I am writing about an argument with my brother:

**angry voices ~ sad smile ~ my things ~ hitting
shouting ~ lying ~ cheating ~ smiling**

Write up your memory.

2 Read your own writing. Answer these questions:

- Which adjectives show the mood of the piece?

- Which verbs do you like? Is the mood clear from the words you've used?

- If your answer to the last question is no, how can you improve your work?

~ Ask the family ~

Ask members of your family what they remember of your childhood. How was their childhood different from yours? What kind of child were you? How have you changed?

Aim:

~To build on the skills acquired in the last homework by using the techniques of successful autobiographical writing in your own work. You will also look at your own writing critically.~

National Curriculum:

~Writing: Range (c) autobiography~

~Writing: Standard English and Language Study (b) analyse own writing~

Background:

~The best autobiography is usually about a time in your life that really mattered to you, a time that you remember clearly.~

Vocabulary:
critical   mood

Spellings:
compare   comparison

67

Aim:

~This homework asks you to gather together realia (real things) that are connected to aspects of your life. You will also explain the significance of your chosen objects to a familiar audience giving reasons for your choices.~

National Curriculum:

~Speaking and Listening: Range (a) explanation~

~Writing: Range (b) to inform others through explanation~

Background

~It is important to recognise that autobiography is closely linked with real-life objects and events.~

Vocabulary:
realia   explanation

Spellings:
complete   completely

Homework Activity 60

1 Select some reasonably small objects that you think best explain your life. You may want to concentrate on how you are now, or perhaps how you were at different stages of your life. If you want to, you can choose all your objects from early childhood.

When you have chosen them, prepare a short speech to deliver to someone at home about each object. Say why you have chosen it. Deliver your speech.

2 Write an explanation for your choice of objects to give to your teacher. It might be best to do this as a list with comments, e.g. Mouse mat – I chose this because it tells you how computers have always been a part of my life.

~ Ask the family ~

Ask someone at home to listen to your speech for Task One. Ask your helper to write a comment in your homework book about how well you spoke. Discuss what objects are important in your helper's life.

Homework Activity 61

1 Look at a story book that you have at home. Choose a paragraph that describes someone doing something.

- Write out this paragraph in your homework book.

- Now underline every adverb that you can find. Remember an adverb will describe the verb.

2 What is the effect of the adverbs that you have found?

- Are they all the same kind of word?

- If not, how are they different? Try replacing some of the adverbs in the passage with different adverbs.

- What is the effect of doing this? Write a list of any words from the paragraph that you think might be adverbs but that you are not sure about.

~ Ask the family ~

Show the list of words that you are not sure about to someone at home. Tell your helper what you are trying to do and ask what s/he thinks. It is not always easy to spot adverbs.

Aim:

~This homework asks you to revise your knowledge of adverbs and to comment on their use in a book that you are reading.~

National Curriculum:

~Reading: Key Skills (a) exploring choice of language~

~Writing: Standard English and Language Study (b) grammatical functions of adverbs~

Background:

~An adverb describes a verb, e.g. The old man walked painfully. The adverb 'painfully' tells you how he walked. 'Walked' is the verb.~

Vocabulary:
adverb   effect

Spellings:
comprehend
comprehension

69

GRAB THAT GRAMMAR 2

Aim:

~ This homework asks you to revise your knowledge of how adjectives, verbs, nouns and adverbs work in a poem. It also asks you to revise similes in poetry. ~

National Curriculum:

~ Writing: Standard English and Language Study (b) grammatical function of nouns etc. ~

Background:

~ This homework builds on your knowledge of words and how they work. If you have a precise understanding of how words work, you will craft your own work more carefully and with greater success. ~

Vocabulary:
precise grammatical

Spellings:
definite definitely

Homework Activity 62

1 Read the following poem:

FIRE

Bright, wild, orange flames
Crackling, roaring, blazing fiercely
Fire

The flickering flames like curling tongues
Dancing, shooting, bursting out
Wild, free, alive.
Fire

Write this poem into your homework book.

- Now underline all the adjectives in one colour, all the verbs in another colour, all the nouns in yet another colour and the simile in pencil.

  This is a 'menu' poem. The first line is adjective, adjective, adjective, noun.

- How would you write all the other lines in the same way?

2 Using this menu, write a poem of your own about your favourite food.

~ Ask the family ~

Ask someone at home to help think up words that fit the menu of the poem.

Homework Activity 63

1 Write the following paragraph into your book, adding the correct punctuation where necessary:

one day the old man walked to the lighthouse he liked it here the view was good the sea came over the rocks with some force the old man smiled he was happy the sun was shining and the grass looked green and bright he talked to the lighthouse keeper who was worried about the weather

2 Write the following paragraph into your book, correcting the incorrect punctuation and adding the correct punctuation. Don't forget that you will need some full stops.

hello said, the lighthouse keeper how. are you it is cold today i am worried that the wind is too strong for the boats dont' worry said the old man i think it will "be sunny. all day the wind is not too strong!

Aim:

~*This homework asks you to revise your knowledge of punctuation, so that you become more aware of its impact in your own writing.*~

National Curriculum:

~*Writing: Standard English and Language Study (b) punctuation*~

Background:

~*Your own writing will be improved by the accurate use of punctuation.*~

~ Ask the family ~

When you have tried on your own, go through the work with someone at home. Ask them to help you decide if the paragraph makes sense or not. Ask your helper to suggest ways of improving the punctuation.

Vocabulary:
punctuation impact
Spellings:
despair desperate desperation

Aim:

~ *This homework asks you to consider the difference between using the active voice and the passive when writing sentences.* ~

National Curriculum:

~ *Writing: Standard English and Language Study (b) principles of sentence grammar* ~

Background:

~ *Sometimes in your writing you will want to say what is happening without saying who is doing it.*

When you say what happens to something, you use the passive voice, e.g. The ice was broken.

When you say who did something, you use the active voice, e.g. Ian broke the ice. ~

Vocabulary:
passive voice

Spellings:
discipline disciplinary

Homework Activity 64

1 Each of the sentences below is written in the active voice. Re-write the sentences in the passive voice, so that you do not have to say who or what did it.

a) Billy opened the gate.

b) The old men washed the dishes.

c) The fat dog bit the postman.

d) An important woman told the children off.

e) The river cut a path through the mountain.

2 Read the following sentences:

Julia Dixon was seen entering the shop. Wayne Porter was killed on the third of February.

- Why are these sentences written in the passive voice? Try to think of a different reason for each sentence.

- Write the sentences in the active voice. What is the difference?

~ Ask the family ~

Ask someone at home to help you find examples of active and passive sentences in books around the home. Write these into your book.

Homework Activity 65

1 Consider the two characters below and their views on foxhunting.

- Write down four more points that Bill, the first character, might make. Draw him with speech bubbles for each argument.

- Now write down four more points that Andy might make. Draw him with speech bubbles as he argues with Bill.

2 Write each character's argument in continuous prose, e.g. *I think that foxhunting is cruel because it … I also consider …* etc.

Write a list of useful words and phrases to help build up the argument before you write out the whole argument, e.g. *However, moreover, it can be argued, some people think, clearly, in conclusion,* etc. You could then use one of these words or phrases at the start of each paragraph.

～ Ask the family ～

Ask someone at home to take one side of the argument, while you take the other. This will help you to come up with the best arguments for both sides.

Aim:

~This homework will help you to think about how arguments are constructed. You will have to invent a number of points for both sides of an argument.~

National Curriculum:

~Speaking and Listening: Range (c) listen attentively to argument~

~Writing: Range (a) extend confidence in writing~

Background:

~The National Curriculum requires you to become skilled in argument writing and to recognise bias.~

Vocabulary:
argument   bias

Spellings:
discuss   discussion

ARGUMENT WRITING 2

Aim:

~ This homework asks you to consider how points of an argument are put together in the form of a letter. You will have to consider both sides of an argument. ~

National Curriculum:

~ Reading: Range (e) letters ~

~ Writing: Range (b) argument ~

Background:

~ Argument writing is a form of writing that the National Curriculum requires you to become skilled at. Here, you are also practising your communication skills in the form of a letter. ~

Vocabulary:
concern   manners

Spellings:
decide   decision

Homework Activity 66

1 Read this letter that might have appeared in the local press.

> Dear Editor,
>
> I write to express my concern about the standard of manners of young people these days. As I walk past the local school gates, I see crisp packets, cigarette packs and much other rubbish left by the students. When I pass a group of these students on the street I am forced into the road, as they never think to make room for me to pass. They shout and jeer and the swearing is absolutely disgusting. It is time that something was done about it!
>
> Yours,
> Disgusted of Hull

Write a letter to the editor that agrees with the argument expressed in this letter. Add other possible points to make about the bad manners of young people today.

2 Write a letter that argues against the one above. First think of all the reasons why young people of today could be considered well-mannered and co-operative.

~ Ask the family ~

Find out what different members of your family think about the manners of young people. Present their case in a speech bubble drawn next to a picture of them or their names.

Homework Activity 67

1 Imagine the following:

The local council is considering building a new road. This would bring more work for local people as businesses would move into the area. Unfortunately, the proposed route for the new road goes straight through your school. If the road went ahead you would have to catch a bus to another school that you do not like.

Someone in your family is a local business person who would get more business if the plans go through.

- Design and produce a leaflet for the campaign against the road.

ROAD TO PROSPERITY

Remember a leaflet has to attract and hold the attention of your audience. Write concisely. You might use bullet points and write important words in large print or in colour, or both. Be creative!

2 Produce a second leaflet that argues the opposite point of view.

Aim:

~This homework helps you to develop your skills of argument writing. You have to construct and express a coherent argument, one that makes sense and that is not easy to dismiss.~

National Curriculum:

~Writing: Key Skills (b) argument writing~

~Writing: Standard English and Language Study (a) use of complex grammatical structures~

Background:

~Argument writing is an important skill in the National Curriculum.~

~ Ask the family ~

Ask someone at home to help you come up with arguments for your leaflets. What is your helper's opinion of your leaflets?

Vocabulary:
concise   proposed

Spellings:
descend   descent

75

Aim:

~In this homework you will find out information at home and report back at school on what you have discovered.~

National Curriculum:

~Speaking and Listening: Range (a) preparing for presentation to audience~

Writing: Range (c) making notes~

Background:

~This homework is a preparation for delivering a short talk to some or all of your class on the subject: 'My (Our) Favourite Holiday(s)'~

Vocabulary:
audience   favourite
holiday

Spellings:
embarrassed
embarrassment

Homework Activity 68

1 Think about the best holiday you have ever had. Decide what you will say about it in a two-minute talk at school.

2 Write some notes that will help you to give your talk. Do not try to write out every word of the talk. Just write down some key words that will help you to remember what you want to say. These notes are not for anyone else to read. You are the only person who needs to understand them.

~ Ask the family ~

Talk to members of your family about their favourite holidays. What made the holidays so enjoyable/memorable? Do they like going to different places, or to the same destination every year? Use some of this information when you plan your talk.

Homework Activity 69

1 Find a travel brochure, either at home or from a travel agent's.

Think about the answers to these questions, and be prepared to discuss them at school.

- What information should be in a travel brochure?
- Does your particular brochure make you want to book a holiday? Why? Why not?
- Is it aimed at young people, families with young children, older people, or some other group?

- Is there anything missing from your brochure?
- Are there any misleading statements in it?

2 Write down your answers to the questions above.

~ **Ask the family** ~

Talk to a few people about the questions above. Include their thoughts in what you write down and/or report back at school.

Do they have any favourite travel companies? If so, why do they like them?

Aim:

~You will examinine a very particular kind of publication: travel brochures.~

National Curriculum:

~Speaking and Listening: Range (a) consideration of ideas ... and the media~

~Reading: Key Skills (c) evaluate sources of information~

Background:

~Travel brochures give you information, and also try to persuade you to spend money. In this homework you have to consider how they set about parting you from your cash!~

Vocabulary:
brochure information
persuade

Spellings:
special especially

77

Aim:

~In this homework you will collect information which would be useful to include in a travel brochure.~

National Curriculum:

~Reading: Key Skills (c) select, compare and synthesise information~

~Writing: Key Skills (b) organise persuasive writing~

Background:

~ You have discovered in the previous homework how travel brochures try to persuade their readers to spend their money. Now it is your turn to produce your own brochure.~

Vocabulary:
attractive   factual
data   library

Spellings:
exclaim   exclamation

Homework Activity 70

1 Use travel brochures, your local library and the school library to gather data.

- Collect information about a country which would make it sound an attractive place to visit.

- You may use a CD-Rom for this activity, if you have access to one.

2 Design a page for a travel brochure.

- Use the facts and figures you have collected.

- Make the words and pictures you use as persuasive as possible, so that readers will definitely want to visit the country you describe.

~ Ask the family ~

Decide which country or resort you will feature on your page.

Ask someone at home for advice on how to use your facts and figures in the most persuasive way.

Try out your travel brochure page on your helper.
Would s/he pay to visit the country you are advertising?
Why?/Why not?

Homework Activity 71

1 Prepare a two-minute talk to persuade your friends at school to book a holiday.

Write down any notes that you will need to help you deliver your presentation.

2 You may decide to use more than just your own voice in your presentation. Prepare tapes, pictures and handouts which you think will make your presentation more persuasive.

~ Ask the family ~

Discuss the content and style of your presentation with someone at home, then try out your presentation on your helper.
Listen to the comments and advice.

Aim:

~In this homework you will prepare and practise your persuasive techniques, so that you can sell the holiday of a lifetime to your friends!~

National Curriculum:

~Speaking and Listening: Range (c) use persuasive techniques in presenting work~

~Reading: Key Skills (c) make effective use of information~

~Writing: Range (c) making notes~

Background:

~You should think not only about the actual language you use, but also about music, pictures and other voices that might persuade your friends to book your holiday.~

Vocabulary:
language   presentation
technique

Spellings:
persuade   persuasion
persuasive

Aim:

~*This homework requires you to read and comment on newspaper writing. You need to identify the main points in a news story and to separate facts from opinions.*~

National Curriculum:

~*Reading: Range (e) texts that convey information*~

Reading: Key Skills (c) select information~

Background:

~*The National Curriculum requires you to read and understand all forms of writing.*

Remember, a fact is something that can be proved to be true, e.g. The world is round.

An opinion is just what someone thinks.

Vocabulary:
fact opinion
distraught heroic
bewildered

Spellings:
foreign foreigner

Homework Activity 72

1 Read the following:

Local petite schoolgirl, Janine, thirteen, scaled a dangerous glass-topped garden wall to rip from the ground Mr Green's prize turnip.

"I was going to win at next week's show with that. Now my hopes are dashed," said a distraught Mr Green.

Eyewitnesses say that it was midnight when a small figure was seen leaping gazelle-like from the top of Mr Green's wall, clutching a large object.

Neighbours gave heroic chase but the wily lass escaped them. It was only when Janine's bewildered mother found an enormous turnip under the pretty teenager's bed that Janine was forced to confess.

Now write down all the **facts** that you learn from this story.

2 Write down all the points in the story which you think are matters of opinion.

~ Ask the family ~

Go through your lists with someone at home. Does your helper agree with your choice? Discuss any differences. Alter your lists if you wish.

80

Homework Activity 73

1 Find a newspaper at home. This might be a daily paper, a weekly paper or perhaps a free paper.

Now answer the following questions about the newspaper:

a) What is the name of the newspaper?

b) How many pages have mainly news stories on them?

c) How many pages have mainly advertisements on them?

d) How many pages are devoted to sports news?

e) What kind of news is found in the rest of the paper, e.g. local, world, national, etc.?

f) What, roughly speaking, is the ratio of pictures to text, e.g. pictures take up about a third of the newspaper?

2 Choose one news story from the paper.

- What happened in the news story?
- Where did the action take place?
- Who is involved?
- What do you notice about the way the story is written?

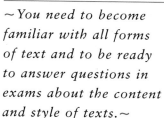

This might be something like:
'The story is local, not very important, but it does name the guilty person. There are a few adjectives in the writing but the sentences are mostly simple. Most sentences begin with a fact.'

~ Ask the family ~

Find out which newspapers your family and friends read and why they choose that particular paper. Write down the results of your research.

Aim:

~This homework builds on the work of Homework Activity 72. Here you are required to find a newspaper and to analyse its contents.~

National Curriculum:

~Reading: Key Skills (c) evaluate how information is presented~

~Writing: Range (b) review~

Background:

~You need to become familiar with all forms of text and to be ready to answer questions in exams about the content and style of texts.~

Vocabulary:
presentation ratio

Spellings:
fright frightened

Aim:

~Here you are asked to apply to your own writing the knowledge that you have acquired about how newspaper stories are written.~

National Curriculum:

~Writing: Range (c) newspaper articles~

~Writing: Standard English and Language Study (c) apt choice of vocabulary~

Background:

~It is important that you practise writing in all the different forms detailed on p.23 of the National Curriculum. The style of any newspaper article differs according to the newspaper for which it is written.~

Vocabulary:
suitable exaggeration

Spellings:
fulfil fulfilled
fulfilment

Homework Activity 74

1 Use the following facts to write a news article that might appear in "The Sun" newspaper:

Man arrested in London
Age: 39
Job: salesman
Crime: suspected of smuggling drugs
Wife has now left him
His son, 14, is in a private school

Remember to use words and sentence lengths that are suitable for "The Sun". Look at a copy of "The Sun" newspaper before you write.

2 Using the same information, write a news article that might appear in "The Daily Telegraph".

Remember to use words and sentence lengths suitable for the newspaper. Look at a copy of the newspaper before you write.

~ Ask the family ~

Read your newspaper articles out loud to someone at home. Can s/he tell which one is written for "The Sun" and which is not? If not, talk about any changes that you could make. Write your helper's comments underneath your articles.

Homework Activity 75

1 Look through the Yellow Pages telephone directory for the names of hairdressers' shops in your area. Choose about twenty interesting names and write them down.

● Read through your list and decide on a way to classify them, i.e. put them into groups. You might group unisex shops together, or ones that use misspelt words (e.g. Kutz). You must have a valid reason for whichever method you use.

2 Write down your reasons for grouping the shops in your method.

● Choose five individual shop names and say why you think the owner has chosen that name.

~ Ask the family ~

Ask people at home which hairdresser they use. Why did they choose that shop? Were they attracted by the name? Which of the names in your list do they find the most eye-catching?

Aim:

~This homework asks you to think about how language can be played with to suggest more than the words say.~

National Curriculum:

~Reading: Standard English and Language Study (a) evaluate characteristic features of texts~
~Writing: Range (b) analysis~

Background:

~It is important that you learn to look at the language used around you with a critical eye and appreciate the humour that shop owners have created through their use of language.~

Vocabulary:
classify method
Spellings:
faithful faithfully

Aim:

~This homework asks you to look at the language of recipes.~

National Curriculum:

~Reading: Standard English and Language Study (a) evaluate characteristic features of texts~

~Writing: Range (b) analysis~

Background:

~It is important that you learn to recognise characteristics of different types of language.~

Homework Activity 76

1 Find a recipe at home. Write down the word at the start of each sentence. What do you notice about these words? Why do you think the sentences begin like this? Are there any adjectives or adverbs? Why are they there/not there?

2 Re-write the recipe as if it were part of a short story. You might start like this: 'The sun blazed through the window as I walked into the kitchen. Feeling rather depressed about my work, I decide to make a lemon meringue pie …'

~ Ask the family ~

Ask someone at home for a favourite recipe. Perhaps you could make it together.

Vocabulary:
recipe
characteristics

Spellings:
guard   guarantee

Homework Activity 77

1 Read this poem by Ben Jonson:

SONG: THAT WOMEN ARE BUT MEN'S SHADOWS

Follow a shadow, it still flies you;
Seem to fly it, it will pursue:
So court a mistress, she denies you;
Let her alone, she will court you.
Say, are not women truly, then,
Styled but the shadows of us men?
At morn, and even, shades are longest;
At noon, they are short, or none:
So men at weakest, they are strongest,
But grant us perfect, they're not known.
Say, are not women truly, then, full grown,
Styled but the shadows of us men?

Read the poem out loud several times. Decide what the poet is saying about women and write it down in your own words. Write whether you agree with Jonson or not, and give reasons for what you say.

2 Write your own reactions in a poem, beginning with the line: Well, Ben, I think you've got it right/wrong …

~ Ask the family ~

Read the poem to someone at home, preferably someone who is a different gender from you. Ask his or her opinion on what Jonson is saying. Try to use some of your helper's ideas in what you write.

Aim:

~In this homework you are asked to agree with, or argue against, the poet and playwright Ben Jonson.~

National Curriculum:

~Reading: Range (d) read major poets writing before 1900~

~Writing: Key Skills (b) develop ability to write poetry~

Background:

~Ben Jonson lived from 1573 to 1637. He was a friend of Shakespeare, and was most famous as a playwright. His plays include "Volpone", "The Alchemist" and "Bartholomew Fair".

Vocabulary:
extended metaphor
playwright

Spellings:
immediate
immediately

Aim:

~In this homework you will write a response to a poem by Christina Rossetti. ~

National Curriculum:

~Reading: Range (d) read major poets writing before 1900~

~Writing: Key Skills (b) develop ability to write poetry~

Homework Activity 78

1 Read this poem by Christina Rossetti:

"NO, THANK YOU, JOHN"

I never said I loved you, John:
Why will you tease me day by day,
And wax a weariness to think upon
With always 'do' and 'pray'?

You know I never loved you, John;
No fault of mine made me your toast:
Why will you haunt me with a face as wan
As shows an hour-old ghost?

I dare say Meg or Moll would take
Pity upon you, if you'd ask:
And pray don't remain single for my sake
Who can't perform that task.

I have no heart? – Perhaps I have not;
But then you're mad to take offence
That I don't give you what I
have not got:
Use your own common sense.

Background:

~Christina Rossetti lived from 1830 to 1894. She wrote a large number of poems and was one of the most popular poets of the Victorian age.~

Let bygones be bygones:
Don't call me false, who owed not to be true.
I'd rather answer 'No,' to fifty Johns
Than answer 'Yes,' to you.

Let's mar our pleasant days no more,
Song-birds of passage, days of youth;
Catch at today, forget the days before:
I'll wink at your untruth.

Let us strike hands as hearty friends;
No more, no less; and friendship's good:
Only don't keep in view ulterior ends,
And points not understood

In open treaty. Rise above
Quibbles and shuffling off and on:
Here's friendship for you if you like; but love, –
No, thank you, John.

● Read the poem aloud several times. Write it in prose, in the language that people might use today.

2 Now write your own poem, rejecting someone.

~ **Ask the family** ~

Read the poem to someone at home. Ask your helper to suggest modern equivalents for what Christina Rossetti says. Have s/he experienced similar situations?

Vocabulary:
prose ulterior
equivalent

Spellings:
invite invitation

Aim:

~In this homework you will write a response to a poem by Gerard Manley Hopkins.~

National Curriculum:

~Reading: Range (d) read major poets writing before 1900~

~Writing: Key Skills (b) develop ability to write poetry~

Homework Activity 79

1 Read this poem by Gerard Manley Hopkins:

"THE CAGED SKYLARK"

As a dare-gale skylark scanted
   in a dull cage
Man's mounting spirit in his
   bone-house, mean house, dwells –
That bird beyond the remembering
   his free fells;
This in drudgery, day-labouring
   out life's age.

Though aloft on turf or perch or poor low stage,
Both sing sometimes the sweetest, sweetest spells,
Yet both droop deadly sometimes in their cells
Or wring their barriers in bursts of fear or rage.

Not that the sweet-fowl, song-fowl, needs no rest –
Why, hear him, hear him babble and drop
   down to his nest,
But his own nest, wild nest, no prison.

Man's spirit will be flesh-bound
   when found at best,
But uncumbered: meadow-
   down is not distressed
For a rainbow footing it nor
   he for his bones risen.

- Hopkins is comparing a caged bird to a human being. Choose another animal and write down some comparisons between your animal and a human being.

2 Turn your comparisons into a poem. Try to create some new words by putting two existing words together, as Hopkins does in 'dare-gale' and 'day-labouring'.

~ Ask the family ~

Read the poem to someone at home. Together, work out what it means. Ask for help in drawing up your list of comparisons between an animal and a human being.

Background:

~Gerard Manley Hopkins lived from 1844 to 1899. He was a Roman Catholic priest. Most of his poems were not published until after his death, mainly because he and his friends thought that the poems were too odd to be accepted by the public.~

Vocabulary:
comparison
invention

Spellings:
invisible   invisibility

89

Homework Activity 80

Read this poem by Emily Dickinson:

"A BIRD CAME DOWN THE WALK"

A Bird came down the Walk
He did not know I saw -
He bit an Angleworm in halves
And ate the fellow, raw,

And then he drank a Dew
From a convenient Grass -
And then hopped sidewise to the Wall
To let a Beetle pass -

He glanced with rapid eyes
That hurried all around -
They looked like frightened Beads, I thought -
He stirred his Velvet Head

Like one in danger, Cautious
I offered him a crumb
And he unrolled his feathers
And rowed him softer home

Than Oars divide the Ocean,
Too silver for a seam -
Or Butterflies, off Banks of Noon
Leap, plashless as they swim.

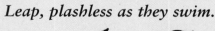

1 Note how the poet carefully describes the movements of the bird. Note particularly the two similes –
'*like frightened beads ...*' and
'*... like one in danger ...*' – and the metaphors, which compare the bird's wings to oars and the bird to a butterfly. Now make some notes about the movements of an animal which you have observed. Try to include some similes and metaphors.

2 Write a poem about an animal, in the style of Emily Dickinson.

Background:

~Emily Dickinson lived from 1830 to 1886. Only seven out of her 2000 poems are known to have been published in her lifetime. From her forties onwards, she became a recluse and refused to leave her home.~

～ Ask the family ～

Read the poem to a someone at home. Ask for help in describing the movements of the animal you have chosen. Read your own poem, and ask if it sounds like the work of Emily Dickinson.

Vocabulary:
metaphor recluse
simile

Spellings:
know knowledge

Aim:

~In this homework you are asked to respond to a nightmare vision, written by Shelley.~

National Curriculum:

~Reading: Range (d) read major poets writing before 1900~

~Writing: Key Skills (b) develop ability to write poetry~

Homework Activity 81

1 Read this selection of verses from "The Masque of Anarchy":

> As I lay asleep in Italy,
> There came a voice from over the sea,
> And with great power it forth led me
> To walk in the visions of Poesy.
>
> I met Murder on the way –
> He had a mask like Castlereagh –
> Very smooth he looked, yet grim;
> Seven bloodhounds followed him:
>
> All were fat; and well they might
> Be in admirable plight,
> For one by one, and two by two,
> He tossed them human hearts to chew,
> Which from his white cloak he drew …
>
> And many more Destructions played
> In this ghastly masquerade,
> All disguised, even to the eyes,
> Like bishops, lawyers, peers, or spies.
>
> Last came Anarchy; he rode
> On a white horse splashed with blood;
> He was pale even to the lips
> Like Death in the Apocalypse …

With a pace stately and fast
Over English land he passed,
Trampling to a mire of blood
The adoring multitude.

And a mighty troop around
With their trampling shook the ground,
Waving each a bloody sword,
For the service of their Lord.

And, with glorious triumph, they
Rode through England, proud and gay,
Drunk as with intoxication,
Of the wine of desolation.

- Read the poem aloud several times, then draw a picture which shows the main images which stay in your mind after the reading. Include some words from the poem in your picture.

2 Choose a public figure of whom you do not approve, and write a few Shelley-like verses about him or her!

Background:

~Percy Bysshe Shelley lived from 1792 to 1822. He was a rebel and a radical, who despised most of the politicians of his day.

"The Masque of Anarchy" was written in response to an event which became known as the Peterloo Massacre, when the government used armed troops to break up a political demonstration in Manchester and six people were killed.

Castlereagh, who is mentioned in "The Masque of Anarchy", was the Prime Minister in 1819, when the poem was written.~

~ Ask the family ~

Ask someone at home to read the poem with you. Use as much scorn in your voices as you can!

Vocabulary:
anarchy masquerade
scorn radical

Spellings:
literate literature

93

Aim:

~ *You will respond to a poem by Elizabeth Barratt Browning about social injustice.* ~

National Curriculum:

~ *Reading: Range (d) read major poets writing before 1900* ~

~ *Writing: Key Skills (b) develop ability to write poetry* ~

Background

~ *Elizabeth Barratt Browning lived from 1806 to 1861. She secretly married Robert Browning, the poet, against her father's wishes, when she was forty years old. She lived most of the rest of her life in Florence, but she was still aware of the injustice of children working in British factories.* ~

Vocabulary:
exploitation
injustice   social

Spellings:
mystery   mysterious

Homework Activity 82

1 Read this extract from "The Cry of the Children":

> *For, all day, the wheels are droning, turning, –*
> *Their wind comes in our faces, –*
> *Till our hearts turn, – our head, with pulses burning,*
> *And the walls turn in their places:*
> *Turns the sky in the high window blank and reeling,*
> *Turns the long light that drops down the wall,*
> *Turn the black flies that crawl along the ceiling,*
> *All are turning, all the day, and we with all.*
> *And all the day, the iron wheels are droning,*
> *And sometimes we would pray,*
> *"O ye wheels" (breaking out in a mad moaning),*
> *"Stop! Be silent for today!"*

● Read the poem aloud several times. Make a list of everything the poem describes as 'turning'. There are seven of them. Now draw a picture that is inspired by your reading of this poem, and include some of the words from the poem in the drawing.

2 Think of a situation in the world today where children are exploited. Write a poem from the point of view of those children. Use one word several times for effect, as Elizabeth Browning uses the word "turn".

~ Ask the family ~

Ask someone at home to read the poem with you. Talk to your helper about child exploitation in the world. Try to use ideas that you discussed in your poem.

Homework Activity 83

1 After the Red Riding Hood story, the Social Services department find out that a little girl has been sent out into the forest on an errand, ALL BY HERSELF!

Write the report of the social worker who visits Red Riding Hood's home. Try to write it in the style that you think fits the situation.

2 Now write briefly about the decisions you made in structuring your social worker's report. Write about the language you used, how you constructed your sentences, and how you expressed the judgements which you came to about this girl's home background.

~ Ask the family ~

Ask someone at home to act out the part of Red Riding Hood's mother or father, while you act the part of the social worker.

Aim:

~You will write in an 'official' style, and then explain how you did it.~

National Curriculum:

~Speaking and Listening: Standard English and Language Study (a) adapt talk to suit circumstances~

~Writing: Standard English and Language Study (a) distinguish between varying degrees of formality~

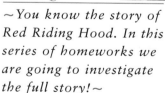

Background:

~You know the story of Red Riding Hood. In this series of homeworks we are going to investigate the full story!~

Vocabulary:
judgement
language   official

Spellings:
murmur   murmuring

ALL THE BETTER TO EAT YOU WITH 2

Aim:

~ You see the story from a different point of view in this Homework Activity, when you are asked to put yourself in the position of the wolf's family. ~

National Curriculum:

~ Speaking and Listening: Standard English and Language Study (a) adapt talk to suit circumstances ~

~ Writing: Key Skills (b) develop ability to write dialogue ~

Background:

~ There are always at least two sides to every story. Imagine how you would feel if you were the wife or child of the wolf, who will never come home again. ~

Vocabulary:
attitude interview personality

Spellings:
necessary necessity

Homework Activity 84

1 The wolf's family wants to tell their side of the story. A television company sends someone to interview them. Write down the dialogue between the family and the television interviewer. You could watch some television interviews before you begin to write.

2 Write about how you used language to reveal the personality of the television interviewer and the family member.

● How did you decide on the questions which the interviewer would ask?

● What in your writing helps to convey the attitude of the wolf's family to the Red Riding Hood events?

~ Ask the family ~

Try out your interviewing technique on someone at home. Now let your helper be the interviewer, while you act as the wolf's relative.

● Who came out best?
● Why?
● What did you learn?

96

Homework Activity 85

1 Red Riding Hood's grandma sells her story to the newspapers. Write her story, in the style which fits the newspaper you have chosen. Illustrate your story.

2 Write about your article.

- How did you decide on your headline?

- How did you match the language you used to the kind of newspaper you were writing for?

Aim:

~This homework asks you to think about the way in which a newspaper would deal with a dramatic exclusive interview.~

National Curriculum:

~ Reading: Range (f) analyse and evaluate material from newspapers~

~Writing: Range (c) write newspaper articles~

Background:

~You will need to decide which kind of newspaper you are writing for. The language you use will be very different in each case, e.g. a mass circulation tabloid like "The Sun", or a broadsheet like "The Guardian".~

~ Ask the family ~

Ask someone at home to let you interview her/him as Red Riding Hood's grandma. Read the article after you have written it, and ask your helper to guess which newspaper it appears in.

Vocabulary:
broadsheet
circulation   tabloid

Spellings:
neighbour
neighbouring

Aim:

~*In this homework you have to think very carefully about how young children speak to each other, and about how you can write that speech down as accurately as possible.*~

National Curriculum:

~*Writing: Standard English and Language Study (a) use non-standard forms for effect*~

Background:

~*Think back to when you were younger – or perhaps you have a younger relative, so that you can observe him/her closely.*~

Vocabulary:
accent dialect
non-standard

Spellings:
potato potatoes

Homework Activity 86

1 When Red Riding Hood goes back to school after the incident with the wolf, all her friends crowd round her in the playground to find out what happened. Write down exactly what she and her friends said. Make your writing sound as much like the speech of young children as you can. Use dialect words, if they are used in your area. Try to imitate local accents in your spelling.

2 Write about your choice of language, dialect and accent. What difficulties did you experience in writing the piece? How successful do you think you have been?

~ Ask the family ~

Ask someone at home for
help in making your written conversation
sound as authentic and realistic as possible.
Read the text back as you
go along.

Homework Activity 87

1 The Headteacher calls Red Riding Hood into her/his room, and asks for an explanation for her absence. Write the conversation which follows. Make it sound as authentic as possible.

2 Write about how you created two very different ways of speaking. How and why does Red Riding Hood speak differently? Can you think of other situations when you may use different ways of speaking? Write a list of examples.

Aim:

~*This homework deals with a conversation, between a pupil and a Headteacher. Think about the tone of the conversation, the vocabulary which the pupil and the Head use and the way each structure their speech.*~

National Curriculum:

~*Speaking and Listening: Standard English and Language Study (a)
use appropriate vocabulary, structure and tone*~

~*Writing: Standard English and Language Study (a)
distinguish varying degrees of formality*~

Background:

~*This conversation will sound very different from the one in Homework Activity 86.*~

Vocabulary:
authentic
formality   tone

Spellings:
patient   patience

~ Ask the family ~

Ask someone at home for her/his memories of being called to the Headteacher's office! Try out a scene with your helper, in which you play Red Riding Hood. Test out your ideas before you write them down.

SPELLING, PUNCTUATION & GRAMMAR

Aim:

~To revise spelling patterns.~

National Curriculum:

~Writing: Standard English and Language Study (a) orthographic features of Standard English~

Background:

~It is important that you spell correctly in order to communicate accurately. Spelling is also assessed in the SATs examination and later in your GCSEs.~

Homework Activity 88

1 The following passage contains some words in italics that are spelt incorrectly. Write down the correct spelling of those words in a list numbered 1–15. Make sure that you put the right word next to the right number, e.g. 1. necessary.

When training a dog it is *neccesary* (1) to show that you mean *bisnes* (2) from the *beggining* (3). I would *advice* (4) you to *adress* (5) the dog in a firm voice. You *canot* (6) be too *patiant* (7) but you must be firm. Set aside a *seperate* (8) time each day when you can *perswade* (9) the animal to be *espesialy* (10) good at following your instructions *faithfuly* (11). Do not be *disaponted* (12) if the dog does not *immediatly* (13) do the right thing. He will soon behave in a *butiful* (14) manner, *belive* (15) me.

2 Create your own spelling test like the one above to give to a friend. Write a short paragraph that makes sense, using as many new words as possible.

Vocabulary:
correct
communicate

Spellings:
explain   explanation

~ Ask the family ~

Ask members of your family what words they found difficult to spell when they were at school. Include some of these words in Task Two.

Homework Activity 89

1 Copy this passage into your book, adding the correct punctuation. Remember that capital letters will also be necessary in places.

hello said the little man who lived down Kellys street isnt it a lovely day today wednesday is always nice for me said kelly because i have my violin lesson on that day she walked off down the road and noticed something strange the post box was being taken away by some odd men

2 Write two more paragraphs to add to this story and use full stops, a question mark, commas, a colon, inverted commas, an apostrophe and brackets.

~ Ask the family ~

Ask someone at home to help you with Task Two. Which punctuation marks do you – and your helper – find most difficult to use?

Aim:

~ *You will be practising punctuation.* ~

National Curriculum:

~ *Writing: Standard English and Language Study (b) punctuation* ~

Background:

~ *If you punctuate accurately, your writing will be clearer.* ~

Vocabulary:
inverted commas
apostrophe   brackets

Spellings:
pursue   pursuit

Aim:

~In this homework you will turn simple sentences into complex ones.~

National Curriculum:

~Writing: Standard English and Language Study (b) sentence structure~

Background:

~A clause is a group of words that contains a finite verb. A finite verb is in a tense, such as the present tense: She kicks, or the past tense: She kicked, or the future tense: She will kick.

Simple sentences have only one clause in them, e.g. Sarah kicked the ball.

Complex sentences have two clauses of unequal importance, e.g. Sarah kicked the ball just as the whistle blew.~

Homework Activity 90

1 Turn each pair of simple sentences into one complex sentence.

a) Sally waited for a bus. It was raining.

b) Sam ran around the playground. The teacher stopped him.

c) I heated the soup. I ate it.

d) I read her a book. She was bored.

e) I watched the television. I was knitting.

2 Listed below, in note form, are some facts about the life of Charles Dickens. Rewrite them in complex sentences.

Father was clerk in Navy pay office. Father imprisoned for debt.

Charles worked in blacking factory to make money for family. He was twelve years old when he worked in the factory.

He remembered horror of factory when writing "David Copperfield".

Became reporter for "Morning Chronicle". Wrote reports on debates in House of Commons for "Morning Chronicle".

Married Catherine Hogarth. Was successful writer by time of marriage.

Vocabulary:
complex
finite verb   simple

Spellings:
privilege   privileged

~ Ask the family ~

Ask someone at home for interesting ways to turn simple sentences into complex ones. Do not be satisfied by linking them with the word "and"!

Homework Activity 91

1 Recall the story of Red Riding Hood. Use your knowledge of the story to complete the following sentences.

a) Red Riding Hood ... , but she ... .

b) Red Riding Hood ... , but the wolf ... .

c) Whenever the wolf ... , he ... .

d) When the wolf ... , Red Riding Hood ... .

e) Red Riding Hood ... , because ... .

f) Because the wolf ... , Red Riding Hood ... .

g) Although Red Riding Hood ... , she ... .

h) Although Red Riding Hood ... , the wolf ... .

i) Considering the fact that the wolf ... , he ... .

2 Now write some similar sentences about Goldilocks and the Three Bears.

Aim:

~You will create complex sentences, using a range of connectives.~

National Curriculum:

~Writing: Standard English and Language Study (b) linking of structures through appropriate connectives~

Background:

~There are many different ways in which you can connect simple sentences in order to make complex ones.~

~ Ask the family ~

Ask someone at home to help you create the most interesting sentences you can.

Vocabulary:
connectives
considering

Spellings:
prejudice   prejudiced
prejudicial

AN INVESTIGATION INTO

Aim:

~In this homework you
need to read part of a
novel very carefully and
to answer questions
which will find out how
clearly you have
understood the ideas
behind the text.~

National
Curriculum:

~Speaking and
Listening: Key Skills (b)
build on ideas of others
to reach a conclusion~

~Reading: Key Skills (b)
reflect on writers'
presentation of ideas~

~Writing: Range (b)
develop thinking
through analysis~

Homework Activity 92

1 Read this dialogue from "Frankenstein" by Mary Shelley:

Frankenstein: *You propose to fly from the habitations of man, to dwell in those wilds where the beasts of the field will be your only companions. How can you, who long for the love and sympathy of man, persevere in this exile? You will return and again seek their kindness, and you will meet with their detestation; your evil passions will be renewed, and you will then have a companion to aid you in the task of destruction. This may not be; cease to argue the point, for I cannot consent.*

Creature: *I swear to you, by the earth which I inhabit, and by you who made me, that with the companion you bestow I will quit the neighbourhood of man and dwell, as it may chance, in the most savage of places. My evil passions will have fled, for I shall meet with sympathy! My life will flow quietly away, and in my dying moments I shall not curse my maker.*

Frankenstein: *You swear to be harmless; but have you not already shown a degree of malice that should reasonably make me distrust you?*

Creature: *How is this? I must not be trifled with, and I demand an answer. If I have no ties and no affections, hatred and vice must be my portion; the love of another will destroy the cause of my crimes … My vices are the children of a forced solitude that I abhor, and my virtues will necessarily arise when I live in communion with an equal.*

- Pretend you are Frankenstein. Write down points for and against creating a female companion for the Creature. Make up your mind whether you would create her or not, and give reasons for your decision.

2 Write detailed answers to these questions.

- What arguments does the Creature use to try to persuade Frankenstein to create a mate for him?

- Do you find the arguments convincing? Why? Why not?

- Which speaker is in control of this discussion? Give reasons for your answer.

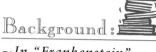

Background:

~In "Frankenstein", Mary Shelley asks the questions: What is it that makes a human being? Will scientists one day have the ability to create life? What will happen if they do?

In the dialogue here, which is taken from the novel, the Creature promises never to return if Frankenstein will make him a female to be his life companion.~

~ Ask the family ~

Ask someone at home to read the dialogue with you – after you have decided who will play the Monster! Together, work out the best answers you can to the questions above.

Vocabulary:
creature detestation
habitation

Spellings:
permanent
permanently

Aim:

~ *You will write about the power of the language of a very famous novel, and to look at the way in which the author creates his dramatic effects.*~

National Curriculum:

~*Speaking and Listening: Key Skills (b) build on ideas of others to reach a conclusion*~

~*Reading: Standard English and Language Study (b) analyse techniques in literature*~

~*Writing: Range (b) develop thinking through analysis*~

Homework Activity 93

1 Read this extract from "Dr Jekyll and Mr Hyde":

Poole swung the axe over his shoulder; the blow shook the building, and the red baize door leaped against the lock and hinges. A dismal screech, as of mere animal terror, rang from the cabinet. Up went the axe again, and again the panels crashed and the frame bounded; four times the blow fell; but the wood was tough and the fittings were of excellent workmanship; and it was not until the fifth that the lock burst in sunder, and the wreck of the door fell inwards on the carpet ...

Right in the midst there lay the body of a man sorely contorted and still twitching. They drew near on tiptoe, turned it on its back, and beheld the face of Edward Hyde. He was dressed in clothes far too large for him, clothes of the doctor's bigness; the cords of his face still moved with the semblance of life, but life was quite gone; and by the crushed phial in the hand and the strong smell of kernels that hung upon the air, Utterson knew that he was looking on the body of a self-destroyer.

- Find phrases in this extract which build up the atmosphere that something is dreadfully wrong. Copy down the phrases, and for each one, write a brief explanation of why you find the words effective in creating this atmosphere.

2 The first paragraph could be summarised in the words: "*Poole swung the axe. They heard a cry. After five blows, the door broke down.*" Why is the actual first paragraph much more effective than the summary? Give as many reasons as you can.

What impression do you get of Edward Hyde from the way in which he is described in the second paragraph? Be as specific as you can.

Background:

~In "Dr Jekyll and Mr Hyde", Robert Louis Stevenson asks the questions: Is every human being a mixture of good and evil? What might happen if the good and evil sides of human beings could be isolated and separated?

In the case of Dr Jekyll, the attempt to answer these questions leads to tragedy. As the story approaches its end, Poole, the servant, and Utterson, the lawyer, break into Dr Jekyll's laboratory and find a dead body.~

~ Ask the family ~

Ask someone at home what effect the particular language chosen by Stevenson has on him/her. This will help you to answer the questions with as much detail as possible.

Aim:

~ You will investigate first impressions: your own and those of the characters in a novel.~

National Curriculum:

~ Speaking and Listening: Key Skills (b) build on ideas of others to reach a conclusion~

~ Reading: Standard English and Language Study (b) analyse techniques in literature~

~ Writing: Range (b) develop thinking through analysis~

Homework Activity 94

1 Read the following extract from "Pride and Prejudice" by Jane Austen:

"Come, Darcy," said he, "I must have you dance. I hate to see you standing about by yourself in this stupid manner. You had much better dance."

"I certainly shall not. You know how I detest it, unless I am particularly acquainted with my partner. At such an assembly as this it would be insupportable. Your sisters are engaged, and there is not another woman in the room whom it would not be a punishment to me to stand up with."

"I would not be so fastidious as you are," cried Bingley, "for a kingdom! Upon my honour, I never met with so many pleasant girls in my life as I have this evening; and there are several of them you see uncommonly pretty."

"You are dancing with the only handsome girl in the room," said Mr Darcy, looking at the eldest Miss Bennet.

"Oh! she is the most beautiful creature I ever beheld! But there is one of her sisters sitting down just behind you, who is very pretty, and I dare say very agreeable. Do let me ask my partner to introduce you."

"Which do you mean?" and turning round he looked for a moment at Elizabeth, till catching her eye, he withdrew his own and coldly said, "She is tolerable, but not handsome enough to tempt me; and I am in no humour at present to give consequence to young ladies who are slighted by other men. You had better return to your partner and enjoy her smiles, for you are wasting your time with me."

- What kind of person is Mr Bingley? Write down some of the words he speaks, and then write what those words tell you about him.

- What kind of person is Mr Darcy? Write down some of the words he speaks, and then write what those words tell you about him.

- Elizabeth Bennet overhears what Mr Darcy says. What would you do next, if you were her?

2 This is the next paragraph of the novel.

Mr Bingley followed his advice. Mr Darcy walked off; and Elizabeth remained with not very cordial feelings towards him. She told the story, however, with great spirit among her friends; for she had a lively, playful disposition, which delighted in anything ridiculous.

- What is Darcy's impression of Elizabeth?

- What is Elizabeth's impression of him?

- Give reasons for your answers.

Background:

~In "Pride and Prejudice", Jane Austen asks the questions: Must we always stay the same as we are now? Are our first judgements about people always correct?

In this extract from the novel, Mr Bingley is holding his first ball at Netherfield Hall. He is dancing with Jane, the oldest of the Bennet sisters. His friend, Mr Darcy, is refusing to dance. Elizabeth, the second Bennet sister, is sitting nearby.~

~ Ask the family ~

Read the extract to someone at home. Ask your helper what s/he thinks about Bingley, Darcy and Elizabeth. Has your helper been in similar situations?

Vocabulary:
judgement   pride
prejudice

Spellings:
recognise   recognize
recognition

AN INVESTIGATION INTO

National Curriculum:

~ *Speaking and Listening: Key Skills (b) build on ideas of others to reach a conclusion* ~

~ *Reading: Standard English and Language Study (b) analyse and discuss alternative interpretations* ~

~ *Writing: Range (b) develop thinking through analysis* ~

Homework Activity 95

1 Read this abridged extract from "The Turn of the Screw" by Henry James:

Miss Jessel stood before us on the opposite bank exactly as she had stood the other time. I remember my thrill of joy at having brought on a proof. She was there, and I was justified; she was there, and I was neither cruel nor mad. She was there for poor scared Mrs Grose, but she was there most for Flora. I threw out to her, pale and ravenous demon as she was, an inarticulate message of gratitude. She rose erect on the spot, and there was not, in all the long reach of her desire, an inch of her evil that fell short.

The revelation then of the manner in which Flora was affected startled me far more than it would have done to find her merely agitated. To see her turn at me an expression of hard, still gravity that appeared to read and accuse and judge me – this was a stroke that somehow converted the little girl into the very presence that could make me quail.

In the immediate need to defend myself, I called passionately, "She's there, you unhappy little thing – there, there, there, and you can see her as well as you can see me!"

110

She was not at these times a child, but an old, old woman. She simply showed me a countenance of deeper and deeper reprobation.

I was by this time more appalled at her manner than at anything else. Simultaneously I became aware of having Mrs Grose to reckon with. My elder companion blotted out everything but her loud, shocked protest. "What a dreadful turn, to be sure, Miss! Where on earth do you see anything?"

- The whole scene is described from the governess's point of view. Rewrite the scene either from Mrs Grose's or Flora's point of view.

2 What evidence is there in the extract to support the view that the governess is unbalanced? Go through the evidence in detail, paying particular attention to the language she uses.

Background:

~In "The Turn of the Screw", Henry James asks the questions: Can we be sure that what we believe to be true is true? Can we ever really understand the thoughts and feelings of another person?

The narrator of the story is a governess who has come to look after the young girl Flora. The previous governess, Miss Jessel, has died in mysterious circumstances. In this extract, the governess and the housekeeper, Mrs Grose, have gone with Flora for a picnic by the side of the river.~

～ Ask the family ～

Read the extract to someone at home. Ask your helper what s/he thinks about the governess's state of mind.

Vocabulary:

narrator reprobation
abridged viewpoint

Spellings:

repeat repetition

Aim:

~ You will look closely at the ways in which a writer's style is constructed. ~

National Curriculum:

~ Speaking and Listening: Key Skills (b) build on ideas of others to reach a conclusion ~

~ Reading: Standard English and Language Study (b) analyse techniques in literature ~

~ Writing: Range (b) develop thinking through analysis ~

Homework Activity 96

1 Read this extract from "Wuthering Heights":

The intense horror of nightmare came over me; I tried to draw back my arm, but the hand clung to it, and a most melancholy voice sobbed, "Let me in – let me in!"

"Who are you?" I asked, struggling, meanwhile, to disengage myself.

"Catherine Linton," it replied, shiveringly. "I'm come home. I'd lost my way on the moor!"

As it spoke, I discerned, obscurely, a child's face looking through the window – Terror made me cruel; and, finding it useless to attempt shaking the creature off, I pulled its wrist on to the broken pane, and rubbed it to and fro till the blood ran down and soaked the bed-clothes: still it wailed, "Let me in!" and maintained its tenacious gripe, almost maddening me with fear.

- Look carefully at the way in which Lockwood describes Catherine. What do his words tell you about the kind of man he is?

  Write your answer to this question with as much detail as you can.

2 Write the answers to these questions with as much detail as you can.

- Why does Lockwood describe Catherine as 'it'? What difference would it make to the tone and atmosphere if he had used the word 'she'?

- Write down all the adjectives in the extract.

- What does your discovery tell you about Emily Bronte's style, and the way in which she creates an atmosphere of horror?

- What difference would it make if the author had narrated the story instead of Lockwood, so that the extract began: *The intense horror of nightmare came over him; he tried to draw back his arm ... ?*

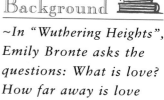

Background

~In "Wuthering Heights", Emily Bronte asks the questions: What is love? How far away is love from hate? Can people recover from damaging experiences and become happy and contented?

The narrator of this extract is Mr Lockwood, who has been forced by bad weather to spend the night at an isolated house, Wuthering Heights. In the middle of the night, he is woken by a tapping on the window. As he watches, a hand smashes through it.~

~ Ask the family ~

Ask someone at home for his/her thoughts on the subject. Discuss situations in which members of your family have experienced a sense of fear or horror.

Vocabulary:
atmosphere
style   tone

Spellings:
separate   separation

FORMS OF WRITING 1

Aim:

~To practise the forms of writing that you need to use confidently in order to do well in the examination. In this homework you practise story writing.~

National Curriculum:

~Writing: Range (a) develop distinctive and original style~

Background:

~Story writing needs to show a conscious choice of words and sentences to create atmosphere and to move the plot forward.

Your story must also be presented in paragraphs.~

Vocabulary:
atmosphere setting

Spellings:
success successfully
succeed

Homework Activity 97

1 Write a story about a teenager who is afraid of something. Show how s/he overcame the fear.

Remember to use adjectives to describe the setting and character.

Write in detail. Make the story come to life. Your reader must be able to picture the place where it is happening and the people to whom it is happening.

When you have finished, check your use of paragraphs, punctuation and spelling.

Make this the best story that you have ever written!

2 Read through your story and pick out some 'good bits'. Write them down and say what is good about them, e.g. *'The dark wood seemed to breathe my fear.'* I think that this is a good bit because it makes the wood sound alive and so makes the atmosphere more scary.

~ Ask the family ~

Ask someone at home about fearful situations. How were these feelings overcome? Take turns to choose a 'good bit' from your story.

Homework Activity 98

1 Imagine that you are the person described below:

This person went on holiday, flying from Gatwick. Unfortunately the plane was ten hours late in taking off. When it finally landed, it had been re-routed to another airport, and the passengers had to travel by rickety old bus for ten hours before they reached their destination. Their luggage arrived four days after they did. However, this person did have the holiday of a lifetime, once s/he got there!

Write a letter to the holiday company complaining about the things that went wrong during your holiday that you felt could have been avoided if the company had been more efficient. Your letter should be formal and polite.

2 Now write a personal letter to a friend of yours, making fun of your disastrous holiday and giving them all your personal news.

Aim:

~*This homework asks you to practise letter writing, both formal and informal.*~

National Curriculum:

~*Writing: Range (c) letters*~

Background:

~*You need to become confident in all forms of writing. The examination might ask you to write a letter.*

A letter can be formal or informal, depending on the person to whom you are writing. You should be familiar with both forms of letter writing.~

~ Ask the family ~

Read both letters to someone at home. Can your helper tell which is the formal letter and which is personal? Have any members of your family experienced any disastrous holidays? Were they able to do anything about it? Can your helper suggest any changes that you agree with?

Vocabulary:
disastrous efficient

Spellings:
straight
straightaway

Aim:

~In this homework you read and comment on a piece of essay or discursive writing.~

National Curriculum:

~Reading: Range (e) issues relating to contemporary life~
~Writing: Standard English and Language Study (b) discourse structure~

Homework Activity 99

1 Read the following and talk to someone at home about what it means:

'HOMEWORK SHOULD BE BANNED.' DISCUSS.

Homework is a description for that work done at home which is rightly in the province of school. It is set by the school and assessed by the school. It could therefore be considered to be something that should be done in school time.

On the one hand, people might argue that children of school age, having worked hard at school all day, should be allowed time for recreation in the evenings. They might also say that, in this day and age, when so much exists for young pepole to do in the way of leisure, it would be more educational for the children to play on their computers or to visit a local sports centre than to repeat boring work that is by its very nature limiting and limited.

However, on the other hand, people might argue that it is only in the peace and quiet of home that the learning begun at school can become confidently understood by the learner. It could be said that without the practice of skills taught at school that day, the children might forget them. One reason for supporting the idea of homework might be that it helps children to learn self-discipline; that by working when they would rather be playing, they are preparing themselves for the difficult demands of adult life.

My own personal belief is in moderation in all things. Children need time to play and, in these busy times, time to spend with their parents or carers. There is little enough time for us all to build relationships and to learn to communicate with those nearest to us. They also need the discipline of meeting deadlines with small amounts of achieveable homework.

2 Identify the words and phrases which help to build the essay, e.g. *On the one hand …*

- Make a list of all such words and phrases.

  Notice that both sides of the issue are discussed.

- How is this form of writing different from persuasive writing?

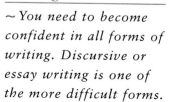

Background:

~ *You need to become confident in all forms of writing. Discursive or essay writing is one of the more difficult forms.*

'Discursive' means to build up a series of arguments, which lead to a conclusion.

This homework asks you to study how discursive writing is put together as a preparation for writing effectively yourself in that form. ~

~ Ask the family ~

Discuss with someone at home their memories of homework. Has it changed? Discuss whether you feel you benefit from homework. What homework do you enjoy most?

Vocabulary:
discursive premise

Spellings:
dependent
independent

WRITING AN ESSAY

~Aim:

~This homework asks you to use the techniques for building discursive essays that you discovered in Homework Activity 99, in order to write an effective essay of your own.~

National Curriculum:

~Writing: Range (c) essays~
~Writing: Standard English and Language Study (b) discourse structure~

Background:

~Discursive essays present a challenge. To write this kind of essay successfully you need to be able to discuss several different and even contrasting ideas on paper.~

Vocabulary:
discussion   phrase
Spellings:
practice   practise

Homework Activity 100

1 The subject under discussion is "Life in Outer Space".

● Make two lists. In the first list, write down all the ideas you and your family can think of for why people believe in life in outer space.

● In the second list, write down all the reasons that you and your family can think of why people do not believe in life in outer space.

● Now make a list of all the words and phrases that could help you to construct your sentences and paragraphs.

2 Before you begin writing your essay, read the example in Homework Activity 99. Now write your masterpiece. Don't worry if it sounds a little clumsy at first; this kind of writing takes practice.

~ Ask the family ~

Discuss with someone at home whether or not they enjoy science fiction books, films or television programmes. Have you or your helper any favourites? What do you enjoy or not like about these programmes? Now ask for some help with Task One.

List of words used in the teaching of English

These words are frequently used in the teaching of English. They occur in the vocabulary lists that appear in the homeworks. You might like to test yourself from time to time, and see if you can explain what they mean.

The words marked * are defined in the glossary on page 121.

abridged	category	*dialect
accent	character	dialogue
accurate	characteristics	diary
action	circulation	dictionary
adverb	climax	direct
advertise	comment	*discursive
advertisement	commentary	discussion
agency	commentator	dissuade
*alliteration	communication	dramatic
analyse	comparison	effect
apostrophe	*complex sentence	effective
appropriate	*compound sentence	encourage
argument	concise	enjoy
atmosphere	conclusion	episode
attitude	*connective	*evaluate
*audience	contrast	exaggeration
*authentic	convey	exciting
behaviour	correct	explain
believable	correspondence	explanation
*bias	critical	*extended metaphor
brackets	decipher	fact
brainstorm	definition	factual
broadsheet	description	favourite
brochure	develop	*finite verb

form

formal

formality

frame

grammar

grammatical

house style

humour

image

imagination

impact

informal

information

instruction

interpretation

interview

invention

inverted commas

issues

journal

judgement

"junk mail"

language

library

mail

*metaphor

method

mime

mood

*narrator

*non-standard English

official

*onomatopoeia

opinion

paragraph

passive voice

perform

personality

persuade

persuasion

*phrase

playscript

playwright

poetic

precise

prejudice

presentation

presenter

*prose

punctuation

purpose

realia

recipe

reflection

relevant

representation

respond

*review

scene

script

selection

sequence

setting

significant

*simile

*simple sentence

speech

staging

*standard English

station identification

storyline

*style

subject

suitable

*syntax

tabloid

target audience

technique

tension

terminology

text

theme

thesaurus

tone

*verb

*viewpoint

Glossary

alliteration
A group of words that begin with the same letters or sounds. Example: *Round the rugged rocks the ragged rascal ran.*

audience
Whenever you write or speak, you need to consider who is your audience, the people to whom you are writing or speaking. What will they understand? What will you need to explain? What will they enjoy?

authentic
In writing or speaking, you will often be asked to make what you say or write sound like something you have studied, like an advertisement or the style of a particular writer. If you manage to make it authentic, it will sound like the real thing.

bias
Sometimes, when they write or speak, people show that they are prejudiced in one way or another. This prejudice is bias. Example: *"The team manager made a statement."* is unbiased; *"The team manager mumbled a statement."* is biased.

complex sentence
A complex sentence is one in which there is at least one subordinate clause. A subordinate clause has a finite verb and begins with a qualifying word, such as *'when'*, *'if'*, *'as'*, etc. Example: *When she had locked the door, she walked down the street.*

compound sentence
A compound sentence is one in which two or more ideas are linked together by a connective. Example: *She locked the door and walked down the street.*

connective
Any word which can be used to join other words together is a connective. Examples: *and*; *but*; *when*; *because*.

dialect
A dialect word is a local word which can be used in place of a standard English word. Example: *"bairn"* instead of *"child"* in the North East of England.

discursive
A discursive essay is one which builds up a set of arguments and then comes to a conclusion.

evaluate

When you evaluate a piece of work or a novel or a poem, you say how good you think it is and give reasons for what you say.

extended metaphor

In a metaphor, you compare one thing to another, without directly saying that it is like the second thing. Example: *The wind howled around the house*. Here, the wind is being compared to an animal. In an extended metaphor, the writer keeps the comparison going. Example: *The wind howled around the house, sniffing out any possible openings, clawing at loose latches*.

finite verb

A finite verb is one which has a subject. Examples: *You always do that*; *The neighbours are a nuisance*; *I will come back tomorrow*.

metaphor

In a metaphor, you compare one thing to another, without directly saying that it is like the second thing. Example: *The ship ploughed through the sea*. Here, a ship is being compared to a tractor.

narrative

A narrative is a piece of talking or writing that gives an account of one or several events.

non-standard English

This phrase is normally used to mean a way of talking or writing which you would not use in the most formal situation. Example: *He's a right tasty geezer*.

onomatopoeia

You are using onomatopoeia when you use a word which imitates a sound. Examples: *thud*; *bang*; *crash*.

phrase

A phrase is a group of words which does not have a finite verb. Examples: *a good night out*; *in the garden*.

prose

Everything that is not poetry is written in prose.

review

When you review your work, you look back over it, consider its good points and how it could be improved.

imile

When you say that something is like something else or as … as something else, you are using a simile. Examples: *He cut through the crowd like a knife through butter*; *The night was as cold as ice.*

imple sentence

A simple sentence has only one finite verb. Example: *She ran in desperate fear through the rapidly darkening wood.*

tandard English

This phrase is normally used to mean a way of talking or writing which you would use in the most formal situation, or when you want to be understood by the greatest number of people.

tyle

In writing, style refers to the particular way in which a particular writer uses language. For instance, Shakespeare's style is very different from Enid Blyton's.

yntax

Syntax refers to the way in which words are ordered in a sentence, so that they make clear sense.

erb

The verb in a sentence is the word or words which tell you what is or what is done. Examples: *I **am** cross*; *She **had been cheated***; *You **will** not **be** here tomorrow.*

iewpoint

Whenever you read something, you need to be aware whose point of view you are listening to. For instance, is the author telling you things in her/his own voice, or through the voice of a character? If a story begins: *Dave was really bored*, the author is giving you information about Dave. If it begins: *I was really bored*, Dave is giving you information about himself.

List of spellings

Here is the full list of all the spellings that are printed on the homework pages. You might like to use this list to test yourself, or you might give the list to someone at home, so that they can test you.

accept	argue	can't	dependent
accident	argument	cause	descend
accidental	autobiography	caution	descent
accidentally	awful	cautious	describe
accommodate	awfully	choice	description
accommodation	beautiful	choose	despair
address	beauty	chose	desperate
addressed	because	compare	desperation
advertise	begin	comparison	diary
advertisement	beginning	complete	disappear
advice	belief	completely	disappoint
advise	believe	comprehend	disciplinary
already	believing	comprehension	discipline
although	biography	conscience	discuss
analyse	bored	conscientious	discussion
analysis	boring	conscious	does
anxiety	bought	consciousness	doesn't
anxious	bring	could	embarrassed
anybody	brought	courage	embarrassment
anyone	business	courageous	especially
apologise	busy	dairy	except
apologize	buy	decide	excited
apology	careful	decision	excitement
appal	carefully	definite	exciting
appalling	cannot	definitely	exclaim

exclamation

explain

explanation

faithful

faithfully

fame

famous

final

finally

foreign

foreigner

friend

friendly

fright

frightened

fulfil

fulfilled

fulfilment

guarantee

guard

handkerchief

handkerchieves

height

high

humorous

humour

immediate

immediately

independent

invisibility

invisible

invitation

invite

know

knowledge

laid

lay

lie

lied

literate

literature

loneliness

lonely

luscious

luxurious

murmur

murmuring

mysterious

mystery

necessary

necessity

neighbour

neighbouring

opposite

opposition

paid

pay

patience

patient

permanent

permanently

persuade

persuasion

persuasive

poem

poetry

potato

potatoes

practice

practise

prejudice

prejudiced

prejudicial

privilege

privileged

pursue

pursuit

quiet

quite

receipt

receive

recognise

recognition

recognize

repeat

repetition

replied

reply

rhyme

rhythm

separate

separation

should

sincere

sincerely

special

stop

stopped

straight

straightaway

succeed

success

successfully

surprise

surprising

tried

try

weather

whether

wonder

wonderful

would

write

writing

Your Notes

Your Notes

Your Notes

Your Notes

Your Notes

Your Notes

Your Notes

Your Notes

Your Notes

Your Notes

Your Notes